Reviews of the authors' other
Golden Ratio & Fibonacci Sequence-themed books

THE GOLDEN RATIO LIFESTYLE DIET

The Golden Ratio Lifestyle Diet is a masterpiece. By uncovering the universal key to health, healing, and beauty, Dr. Friedman and Matthew Cross have unlocked a "secret" formula that can help us transform each area of our lives so that quality longevity is within the reach of every human being. **This book deserves a Nobel Prize in medicine.**

Ann Louise Gittleman, Ph.D., C.N.S., NY Times Bestselling Author of *The Fat Flush Plan* and *Your Body Knows Best*

For millennia scientists have noted significant mathematical relationships that seem to optimize function. In this landmark book, these relationships have been extended to optimizing our lifestyle. Obviously, we are all genetically unique, so one size does not fit all. However there are limits beyond certain mathematical relationships where performance drops. This book provides an excellent starting point to retake control of your life by finding those limits. **I strongly recommend it.**

Dr. Barry Sears, Health & Longevity Pioneer; Phenomenal Bestselling Author of *The Zone* book series

THE MILLIONAIRE'S MAP™

Sometimes I feel the need to share something that has impacted my life for the better. The Millionaire's MAP™ has been a profound experience that keeps on unfolding in more and more wonderful ways. Along with other personal processes, this book has helped me to see there are truly no limits to prosperity. It is not about how much money you have in the bank, it is a deep knowing that the universe is vast and unlimited. This book can be used again and again by anyone in any situation… and it works. Even if you do not believe in such things. This is not just a book to read, but to do. It is fun and inspiring. **I recommend you get this book for anyone you truly care about and would like to see living a more prosperous life.**

Gurumarka Khalsa, Master Yogi, Lifestyle Enhancer and Author, *Total Fitness*

The Millionaires MAP™ is the most powerful prosperity tool I've yet to encounter in 20 years of studying money and personal development. It opened my eyes to my best financial future, and it opened my heart to my highest, greatest, grandest values because it also acts as an extraordinary clarifier of your passions. And I must add this: For the first time in my life I feel completely open and ready to receive millions, and I've never had so much fun with money as I did while working through the book's easy daily exercises. I highly recommend The Millionaires MAP to all my friends, because it works profoundly on so many levels. Thank you Matthew!

Patrick Combs, President, Good Thinking Company; Speaker, Performer and Bestselling Author, *Major In Success* and *Man 1, Bank 0*

THE DIVINE CODE OF DA VINCI, FIBONACCI, EINSTEIN & YOU

In The Divine Code, Matthew Cross and Dr. Robert Friedman take one of Creation's great secrets and make it accessible, engaging and fun. This book offers you a cornucopia of delightful insights, enlivening practices and inspiring "A-ha's"!

Michael J. Gelb, Renaissance Man and Bestselling Author, *How to Think Like Leonardo Da Vinci* and *Da Vinci Decoded*

A stunning masterpiece. I just re-read the The Divine Code, this time to savor its exquisite intricacies. The Code is interwoven into all of life, into everything we are, into everything we do. To understand it is to understand the very fabric of our being. To live its principals is to live in harmony with all that is. Cross and Friedman have created a timeless resource and a grand guide—the ultimate guide—to success in all we endeavor to experience and accomplish in our lives.

Walter R. Hampton, Jr., Attorney, Speaker and Bestselling Author, *Journeys On The Edge: Living A Life That Matters*

Enhancing Cognition and Genius: A Study In Golden Ratio Design

Designing with the Golden Ratio supports the symmetry and attractiveness of the medium's ability to enhance the message. The Golden Ratio is hardwired into our bodies all they way down to our DNA; it infuses all of our perceptive senses, including sight and sound. We are naturally drawn to and delight in its appearance, which serves to enhance the efficiency and speed of our information processing and cognition.

With the Golden Ratio renaissance currently re-emerging, enlightened designers are beginning to rediscover these design concepts (see page 50 for how this enhances web design). For the cover of this book, after the initial mock-up sketch the key design elements were set in place with an eye towards the Golden Ratio 1.618:1, using PhiMatrix™ software (red grid). Natural Golden Ratios present in the sunflower's spiraling seeds were also integrated into the overall page layout.

Even one Golden Ratio design element enhances the overall design; two or more adds an embedded, exponential effect in support of the Golden Ratio's unity function––bringing parts together into a greater whole. Yet quantity is not the aim; the right balance of quality and quantity of the Golden Ratio for the design is the key. Additional natural Golden Ratios, e.g., the sunflower petal length to face diameter, helped to achieve this balance. This approach is continued into the design layout of the book's inside pages. It's no coincidence that Apple selected the sunflower, a universal and multifaceted icon of the Golden Ratio, as its photo album icon for the iPhone and iPad iOS. As legendary Canadian media and communication theorist Marshall McLuhan said,

> Societies have always been shaped more by the nature of the media by which men communicate than by the content of the communication…
> The Medium is the Message.

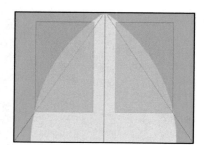

The Timeless Design Canon

The utilization of the Golden Ratio as a design canon spans from ancient to modern times, as can be seen in the 3000 year-old Tablet of Shamash all the way up to Twitter's website design (see page 50). In his *The Form of the Book*, master typographer Jan Tschichold depicts the Canon of Golden Ratio proportions in a medieval manuscript: page proportion 2:3; margin proportions 1:1:2:3; text area proportioned in Golden Ratio. According to Tschichold,

> there was a time when deviations from the truly beautiful page proportions 2:3, 1:√3, and the Golden Section were rare. Many books produced between 1550 and 1770 show these proportions exactly, to within half a millimeter.

One of this book's aims is to continue where Tschichold and other classical designers and typographers left off, inspiring and empowering modern-day graphic designers to access the power of the Golden Ratio.

The GOLDEN RATIO &
FIBONACCI SEQUENCE

Golden Keys to Your Genius,
Health, Wealth & Excellence

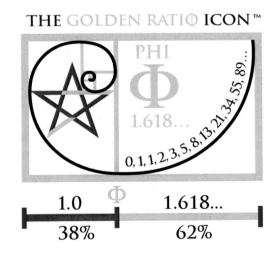

THE GOLDEN RATIO ICON™

PHI

Φ

1.618…

0, 1, 1, 2, 3, 5, 8, 13, 21, 34, 55, 89…

1.0   Φ   1.618…
38%   62%

MATTHEW CROSS &
ROBERT FRIEDMAN, M.D.

The Golden Ratio & Fibonacci Sequence: Some Historical Luminaries

Pythagoras (c. 570–500 B.C.E.) is the archetypal original master mathematician of the Golden Ratio, which he called *The Secret of the Universe*; his secret society's sign was the Golden Star.

Theano (c. 546–480 B.C.E.), mathematician and wife of Pythagoras; recognized as the first woman in recorded history to have written about the Golden Ratio in her book *Theorem of the Golden Mean*.

Phidias (c. 480–430 B.C.E.), Greek sculptor and architect, contributed to the construction of the Parthenon; utilized the Golden Ratio in his work.

Plato (c. 428–347 B.C.E.), classic Greek philosopher; student of Socrates and the Pythagoreans and Aristotle's teacher; believed that the Golden Ratio was *The Most Binding of All Mathematical Relations*.

Pingala (4th century, B.C.E.) and other Indian mathematicians are among the first to elucidate the mysterious number sequence known as the Fibonacci Sequence.

Euclid (c. 323–285 B.C.E.), the Father of Geometry provided one of the earliest geometrical demonstrations of the Golden Section.

Hildegard von Bingen (1098–1179), mystic, monastic leader; composed sacred musical compositions richly infused with the Golden Ratio.

Leonardo Fibonacci (c. 1170–1250), master mathematician of the Middle Ages; first elucidated to the West the infinite mathematical sequence (0,1,1,2,3,5,8,13...) bearing his name, along with zero, Hindu/Arabic numbers and the decimal point.

Fra Luca Pacioli (1445–1517), Father of modern accounting and Da Vinci's mentor; coined the term *Divine Proportion*.

Leonardo Da Vinci (1452–1519), the original Renaissance Man; coined the term *Sectio Aurea* (Golden Section). Da Vinci utilized the Divine Proportion in artistic works that would become instantly recognizable worldwide, e.g., *The Vitruvian Man* famously shows Divine Proportions in the human body. *The Mona Lisa*, the world's most famous and recognized painting, contains many Divine Proportions.

Michelangelo (1475–1564) master Renaissance artist; timelessly captured humanity's Golden Proportions in his paintings and sculptures, most notably in the Sistine Chapel and in his classic sculpture *David*.

Johannes Kepler (1571–1630), scientist; expounded the laws of planetary motion and was fascinated by the Golden Ratio, calling it *Geometry's Most Precious Jewel*.

Descartes (1596–1650), the "I think, therefore I am" philosopher; used the term *Equiangular* to describe the Golden Spiral.

Jakob Bernoulli (1654–1705), scientist; used the term *Spira Mirabilis* (Magic Spiral) to describe the Golden Spiral.

Robert Simson (1687–1768), mathematician; correlated the Golden Ratio with the Fibonacci Sequence.

Charles Bonnet (1720–1793), botanist; observed that the ratios of counter-rotating spirals in plants mirrors adjacent Fibonacci numbers.

Thomas Jefferson (1743–1826), American president and author of the Declaration of Independence; incorporated the Golden Ratio into the University of Virginia's Rotunda design.

Martin Ohm (1792–1872), mathematician; uses the term *Der Goldene Schnitt* (The Golden Cut) in reference to the Golden Ratio.

Gustav Fechner (1801–1887), psychologist; demonstrated that the perception of beauty reflects Divine Proportion.

Edouard Lucas (1842–1891), mathematician; first to refer to Fibonacci's numerical progression as the *Fibonacci Sequence*.

Ralph Nelson Elliott (1871–1948), accountant; first uses Fibonacci Ratios in stock market analysis, known as Elliott Waves.

Frank Lloyd Wright (1876–1959), master architect; used the fractal principle of the Golden Ratio in his classic architectural designs over a wide range of scales.

Albert Einstein (1879–1955), genius of the ages; stated in a letter to famed architect Le Corbusier that *the Divine Proportion is a scale of proportions which makes the bad difficult and the good easy.*

Le Corbusier (1887–1965), master architect; created *Le Modulor*, which utilizes Golden Ratio relationships of the human structure to optimize architectural design.

R. Buckminster Fuller (1895–1983), a 20th century Copernicus, inspired the discovery of the Buckminsterfullerene or BuckyBall, a Golden Ratio-rich molecule and universal building block.

Mark Barr (19th century), mathematician; first used the term *Phi* Φ to describe the Golden Ratio, after the Greek architect Phidias, who contributed to the Parthenon's creation. Prior to this, the Golden Ratio was more accurately referred to by the Greek letter *Tau* τ—meaning [Golden] *Section*—directly reflecting this in its 1.618:1 vertical:horizontal ratio lines.

20th/21st Century Luminaries

Arthur Jones invented Nautilus® exercise equipment, which incorporates the Golden Spiral in function and design.

Walt Disney imprinted his classic cartoon characters and movies with Golden Ratio design and themes. In *Donald Duck in Mathmagic Land* (1959), Donald Duck meets Pythagoras and explores many mysteries of the Universe, including the Golden Ratio.

John Michell, master geometer and author who unearthed many profound Golden Ratio connections throughout ancient and modern history.

HRH Prince Charles emphasizes Nature's laws of sacred geometry, including the Golden Ratio, as touchstones for personal and planetary renewal in his book, *Harmony: A New Way of Looking at the World*.

Robert R. Prechter, Jr., expanded the predictive patterns of the Fibonacci Ratio/Elliott Wave principle into social, behavioral and economic theory. This new field is known as *Socionomics*.

Dr. Ronald Sandler created a system utilizing Fibonacci Ratios/Elliott Waves for injury free and predictable peak athletic performance.

Steve Jobs, Apple Inc. co-founder, revolutionized the world with Golden Ratio-imprinted products that empower and inspire people to express their creative genius to *Make a Dent in the Universe*.

Steve Wozniak, Apple Inc. co-founder, was inspired by the Fibonacci Sequence and is renowned for the elegant simplicity of his software and hardware designs.

Stephen McIntosh is an integral theorist who used Fibonacci ratios for gentle awakening in a beautifully designed alarm clock: *The Zen Alarm Clock*.

Jonathan Ive, is the award-winning lead designer for Apple Inc. who incorporates Golden Ratio design elements into cutting-edge Apple products.

Collin Nicholas Saad, aka **Jain** is a mathemagician who demonstrated that the infinite Fibonacci Sequence has discernible repeating macro-patterns.

Drs. Yosh Jefferson, Eddy Levin, David Frey are shifting the prevailing paradigm for dentists by using the Golden Ratio in aesthetic and restorative dentistry.

Anastasia Soare revolutionized the field of facial aesthetics and natural beauty enhancement with her ingenious utilization of the Golden Ratio in eyebrow sculpting.

Hanno Ulmer, Ph.D. statistically proved that blood pressure values in well individuals, but not in those who are at risk of dying, exhibit the Golden Ratio.

Michael Schneider steps out as a prime ambassador for the Golden Ratio and sacred geometry with his classic book, *A Beginner's Guide to Constructing the Universe*.

Ronald Holt eloquently links the Fibonacci Sequence and Golden Ratio as complimentary elements of our conscious spiritual evolution, a Golden Bridge to our potential and perfection.

Steven Marquardt, M.D. developed the Golden Ratio-based Beauty Mask as an ideal template for plastic surgeons, dentists and make-up artists to enhance facial beauty.

Gary Meisner developed the PhiMatrix,™ an elegant and easy to use graphic design and analysis software program based on the Golden Ratio.

Mario Livio is an astrophysicist who wrote a top non-fiction Golden Ratio book, *The Golden Ratio: The Story of PHI, The World's Most Astonishing Number*.

J.K. Rowling ingeniously used the homonym of the *Golden Snitch*, i.e., *Goldene Schnitt* (Golden Ratio in German) in her hugely popular Harry Potter books and films—among the most successful in history—to subtly convey the illusive, infinite and priceless nature of the Golden Ratio to the world.

Dan Brown's *The Da Vinci Code* is another top selling book (80 million copies sold as of 2013) and film to popularize Phi Φ and the Fibonacci Sequence. *Note: Both J.K. Rowling's & Dan Brown's Golden Ratio-tinged books and films are among the most successful in history, with combined sales of well over 13 billion dollars. As Matthew Cross says, Good Fortune Follows the Golden Ratio...*

Ruth & Sara Levy are the creators of *The Fashion Code*, the first total wardrobe optimization system utilizing the Golden Ratio.

Twitter and **Siemens** broke the traditional mold by incorporating the Golden Ratio into their website designs for increased traffic and a more enjoyable viewing experience.

Apple, Toyota, Google, Starbucks, Twitter and many other cutting-edge companies have embedded Golden Ratios in their logos, which enhance their brand and customer appeal.

Robert Friedman, M.D. & Matthew Cross first integrate the Golden Ratio and Fibonacci Sequence into a complete, practical system for achieving and maintaining robust health and longevity in their acclaimed book, *The Golden Ratio Lifestyle Diet*.

Matthew Cross & Robert Friedman, M.D. are the first to utilize the Fractal Cognition™ approach to present the essence of the Golden Ratio & Fibonacci Sequence to the world, via this book...

Opposite page: The Golden Ratio in many terms and languages, a rose by any other name.

This book is dedicated to
the Golden Ratio genius and infinite potential within you...

I study the Patterns of the Universe.

Will Smith

Disclaimer ~ Nota Bene

The information and/or recommendations in this book are not meant to diagnose, treat or cure any medical condition. Before trying or experimenting with any of the nutritional recommendations, exercise protocols, health improvement or any other health-related suggestions described in this book, consult your physician or health care professional. The reader assumes 100% complete responsibility for any/all interpretations they may have and/or actions they may take and/or results they may enjoy as a result of reading this book. Neither the Publisher nor the Authors are liable for any loss, injury, damage or misunderstanding, which may occur from any interpretation and/or application of any of the information within this book. The quotes featured within this book are from numerous sources, and are assumed to be accurate as quoted in their original and/or previously published formats. While every effort has been made to verify the accuracy of featured quotes, neither the Publisher nor the Authors can guarantee or be responsible for their perfect accuracy. All websites, URLs and telephone numbers within this book were accurate at time of publication. However, websites may be modified or shut down and URLs or telephone numbers may change after publication without notice. Therefore, the Publisher and Authors are not responsible in any way for the content contained in or missing/modified within any specific web site featured within this book. This book was created to be a holographic, gestalt approach to understanding and applying the Golden Ratio principles explored within it. The authors' insights, conjectures and conclusions reached within this book are theirs alone, and—however provocative and mind-expanding they may be—may not be endorsed by any of the people or organizations referenced within this book. No endorsement or sponsorship of this book, either in whole or in part, by any registered trademark and/or service mark and/or copyright owners and/or person(s) featured in this book is inferred or implied by their being featured in this book; all are featured for educational/illustrative purposes only. The authors enthusiastically endorse all of the organizations, their products and/or services featured within this book. iPhone,® iPad® are trademarks of Apple Inc.; Hotel Indigo is a trademark of InterContinental Hotels Group, Inc.; Toyota/Lexus are trademarks of the Toyota Motor Corp.; Starbucks is a trademark of Starbucks Corp.; National Geographic is a trademark of National Geographic, Inc.; *Donald in Mathmagic Land* is a trademark of The Walt Disney Company, Inc.; Pac-Man is a trademark of Namco Bandai; Google is a trademark of Google Inc.; any/all other trademarks and/or service marks and/or copyrights featured in this book are the property of their respective owners.

Made on a Mac: this book was written and designed on the incomparable computers made by the talented people of Apple Inc. Thank you Steve & Steve and team Apple for your timeless genius.

Copyright ©2013 by Matthew Cross and Robert Friedman, M.D.; All Rights Reserved. No part of this book may be reproduced in any media without prior written authorization from the publisher. The Golden Ratio Lifestyle Diet,™ Nature's Secret Nutrient,™ The Divine Code,™ The Golden Ratio Icon™ and The Fibonacci WorkoutWave™ are trademarks of the authors; The Millionaire's MAP™ and Fractal Cognition™ are trademarks of Matthew Cross. Book master concept, design and direction by Matthew Cross; original front and back cover concept/design Copyright ©2013 by Matthew Cross, optimized with and rendered by graphic design master Tom Reczek of 618Design.com • Contributing Editor: Diana Doroftei.

Publishing Data: Published in the United States of America by:
Hoshin Media, P.O. Box 16791, Stamford, Connecticut 06905 USA

www.HoshinMedia.com

Copies of this book can be purchased in quantity at a courtesy discount for special business, sales or promotional purposes. Contact Hoshin Media for more information.

Yale professor emeritus Edward R. Tufte (who's been called *The Da Vinci of Data* and *The Galileo of Graphics*) and Steve Jobs' legendary Zen design focus wisdom contributed greatly to the design aesthetic of this book. Tufte references the Golden Ratio in his optimal design teachings. His approach has been summarized in 4 words: *Simple Design, Intense Content,* which elegantly reflects the science of Fractal Cognition.™

The cover title of this book is set in the Golden Ratio-resonant TRAJAN font, directly based on the letters inscribed on the still-standing 98-foot high Trajan's column in Rome, completed in 113 A.D. Constructed by the architect Apollodorus of Damascus by order of the Imperial Roman Senate, the column honors Roman Emperor Trajan and his victorious campaigns, e.g., against the Dacians, the pre-Roman inhabitants of present-day Romania. 2000 years later, Trajan's font has become a most popular choice for the world's top movie posters (e.g., *Titanic*) television show titles and book covers.

CONTENTS

Learn how to see. Realize that everything connects to everything else.

Leonardo Da Vinci

13 Key Qualities of the Golden Ratio and Fibonacci Sequence

1. Golden Keys to genius, universal wisdom and excellence in any endeavor; ignites the imagination.

2. Universal Blueprint; guides the form and function of energy, matter, motion and life.

3. Ubiquitous; found virtually everywhere, from the atomic to the galactic.

4. Value, Quality and Growth; foundational principle for exponential growth, in both quality and quantity.

5. Nature's Path of Least Resistance and Maximum Performance; the efficiency flow code.

6. Unifying and connecting, links all creation; integrates parts into a greater whole.

7. Infinite; Nature's premier irrational number 1.618... can only be approximated with fractions.

8. Mysterious, magical, magnetic; keen fascination of geniuses throughout history.

9. Beauty, harmony, pleasure, grace; where the Golden Ratio is found, so too are these qualities.

10. Timeless; appears as a powerful archetype in civilizations across time.

11. Evolutionary; profound path for growth, continuous improvement and transformation.

12. Open Secret; freely available to anyone, anytime.

13. Divine; spiritual tool for contemplating and connecting with the infinite.

Introduction

The impulse of all movement and all form
is given by Phi Φ [the Golden Ratio].

Schwaller de Lubicz

Albert Einstein's discovery of the Fibonacci Sequence at age 13 unleashed his world-transforming genius: *The Divine Proportion… makes the bad difficult and the good easy.*

What are the Golden Ratio and Fibonacci Sequence and What's In It For You?

This book is your Golden Key for discovering a universal secret previously known only to geniuses such as Pythagoras, Da Vinci and Einstein. This timeless secret is evident in their work and was a prime inspiration that awakened their innate wisdom. A key difference between them and you is that they accessed the secrets: the power of the Golden Ratio and Fibonacci Sequence. This book is a primer for you to access this transformative power in your life. It offers simple examples of how Nature and geniuses throughout history have used Golden Ratio and Fibonacci Sequence principles in countless ways to create the spectacular array of beauty, harmony and success around us. The Golden Ratio is not limited to obscure mathematical concepts or designs; on the contrary, it has infinite applications in virtually every field and venture of mankind. In the chapters ahead, you'll journey through 16 portals of the Golden Ratio and Fibonacci Sequence's ubiquitous appearances throughout heaven and Earth. Once grasped, the essence of the Golden Ratio will ignite your innate creative genius, inspiring you to manifest excellence in any endeavor.

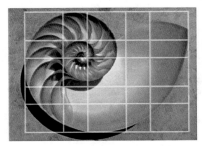

The iconic Nautilus shell is a graceful logarithmic spiral and although not a Golden Spiral, it exhibits multiple Golden Ratio harmonics in its design.

Every rose is a double reflection of the Golden Ratio: Golden Spiral petal patterns in front and a Golden Star on the back.

The Golden Ratio: Nature's Universal Success Code

The Golden Ratio is Nature's universal design fractal. It defines a beautiful, super-efficient relationship or ratio between any two parts or objects where the whole is greater than the sum of its parts. Mathematically known as the ratio 1.618 to 1, the Golden Ratio can be simply expressed in one line, literally. There is only one possible way a line can be divided such that the ratio of the length of the whole line to the large segment is the same as the ratio of the large segment to the short segment. Amazingly, this unifying ratio can only equal 1.618:1, the Golden Ratio, a.k.a. the Golden Mean, Golden Section, Divine Proportion or simply Phi Φ (after Phidias, master Greek sculptor and Parthenon architect who utilized the Golden Ratio) or Tau τ. The ultimate unity code, it integrates the necessary parts or ingredients within any "wholes"

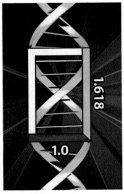

DNA reveals Nature's sacred life geometry. The double helix's length-to-width helical structure is in Golden Ratio. The Pattern of Life thus blueprints the Divine Code of Life.

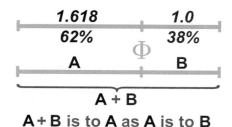

A + B is to A as A is to B

Only when segments of a line or measure assume Golden Ratio relationships to one another does a special unity occur, where the whole exceeds the sum of its parts.

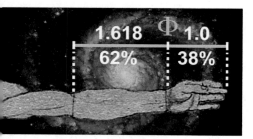

The Golden Ratio is as close as your arm and hand.

Golden Spiral galaxies are one of Nature's grandest signs that we live in a Golden Ratio-based Universe.

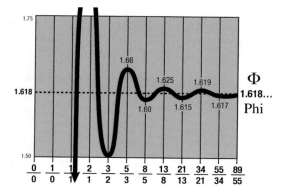

Golden Ratio Pulse Graph. The ratios between successive numbers in the Fibonacci Sequence forever converge on Phi Φ, the Golden Ratio 1.618...

or aims we seek into higher states of quality, beauty, unity and delight. From the multiple elements within health and diet, relationships, financial pursuits, creative endeavors—any and all states can be tuned and optimized through simple application of the Golden Ratio unity principle. The line diagram at left is a powerful Golden Ratio fractal, demonstrating a simple yet profound relationship where two elements come together in a special harmony and unity. This basic Golden Ratio is so fundamental that all other Golden Ratio concepts and designs either flow or can be derived from it. A practical example of the Golden Ratio line diagram is as close as your hand. In the idealized human, the length of the forearm measured from elbow to wrist is about 1.618 times as long as from the wrist to middle fingertip. In other words, the bones of the forearm, hand and fingers are in approximate Golden Ratio to one another. If you measure the lengths of other bones in your body relative to one another, you'll discover that many are also in approximate Golden Ratio to one another. Realize that you carry Nature's master design code within your body's form and function everywhere you go throughout your entire life.

The Fibonacci Sequence: Stairway To Infinite Potential

The following magical sequence of numbers was introduced to the western world in mathematician Leonardo Fibonacci's classic book, *Liber Abaci* (1202). Later named in his honor, this infinite sequence is formed by simply adding one number to the next, beginning with zero:

$$0, 1, 1, 2, 3, 5, 8, 13, 21, 34, 55, 89, 144, 233, 377, 610...$$

The Golden Ratio or Phi Φ is a special, infinite value, closely related to the Fibonacci Sequence and very close to the ratio of its successive terms. If you graph the ratios of adjacent Fibonacci Sequence Numbers, you'll see that they forever converge on one Golden target: the Golden Ratio 1.618... The resultant Fibonacci Ratios dance around the Golden Ratio, with the first ratio lower than 1.618... and the next ratio higher than 1.618..., ad infinitum:

$$1/1=1, 2/1=2, 3/2=1.5, 5/3=1.66, 8/5=1.6, 13/8=1.625,$$
$$21/13=1.615, 34/21=1.619, 55/34=1.617, 89/55=1.618...$$

This is Nature's way of honing in on the elusive perfection of the Golden Ratio, which can only be approximated, as it's an infinite, irrational number. Either way, the advancing Fibonacci Sequence quickly reveals two very special numbers: 1.618, or 0.618 if you invert the ratio. Scott Olsen, author of *The Golden Section: Nature's Greatest Secret*, points out some of the many fascinating aspects of the Fibonacci Sequence: *it is both additive, as each number is the sum of the previous two, and multiplicative, as each number approximates the previous number multiplied by the Golden Ratio. The ratio becomes more accurate as the numbers increase. Inversely, any number divided by its smaller neighbor approximates the Golden Ratio, alternating as more or less than the Golden Ratio, forever closing in on the divine limit.* Like perfection, the Golden Ratio belongs to the realm of the ideal; we are always striving for it, even if we may never reach it. In this sense the Golden Ratio and infinite Fibonacci Sequence are like twin guiding stars, beckoning us onward to discover and share our greater, perfected potential. This concept of infinite expansion towards an ideal is elegantly illustrated by Steve Jobs' suggestion to *Dream Bigger*, when asked by an associate how to improve an important project.

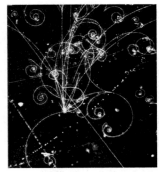

Atoms dancing in Golden Spirals, as seen in an atomic bubble chamber.

The Divine Blueprint of the Universe and Life

The Golden Ratio and Fibonacci Sequence are the fundamental mathematical and geometric principles behind the structure and movement of life and matter in the Universe. As you'll discover, they express themselves in many wonderful ways. When applied to anything, they always create greater efficiency, harmony and success—a greater unified whole exceeding the sum of its parts. The primary facets of the Golden Ratio and Fibonacci Sequence are:

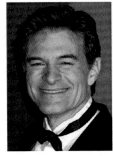

Dr. Mehmet Oz (above) and Dr. Michael Roizen have helped to popularize the Golden Ratio in health, beauty and longevity, via their *YOU* medical book series and on Dr. Oz's popular television show.

The Golden Ratio 1.618:1, more simply 62:38 (62% to 38%)

$$\overset{1.618...}{\underset{62\%}{\rule{4cm}{0.4pt}}}\ \Phi\ \overset{1.0}{\underset{38\%}{\rule{2cm}{0.4pt}}}$$

The Fibonacci Sequence, where the ratio between adjacent numbers forever approaches the Golden Ratio 1.618...,

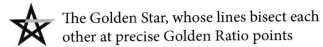

$$\underset{\text{1.60}\qquad\qquad\text{1.619}\qquad\text{1.618...}}{0,\ 1,\ 1,\ 2,\ 3,\ 5,\ 8,\ 13,\ 21,\ 34,\ 55,\ 89\ldots}$$

◻ The Golden Rectangle, whose length-to-width ratio is 1.618:1

◎ The Golden Spiral, where each complete, 360° spiral turn is 1.618 times larger than the previous

☆ The Golden Star, whose lines bisect each other at precise Golden Ratio points

△ The Golden Triangle, whose side-to-base ratio is 1.618:1; it blueprints Golden Stars.

Hurricanes are one of Nature's most powerful examples of Golden Spirals in motion.

Pinecones' modified leaves form counter-rotating spirals that are in Fibonacci Ratio, in this case 8:13.

Fractals are parts containing the pattern of the whole from which they came, broccoli being a good example. The Golden Ratio is Nature's master design fractal, a universal principle of self-similarity found throughout the Universe at every scale, from the galactic to the sub-atomic.

Every ocean wave follows Nature's Golden Spiral path of least resistance.

Da Vinci's *Vitruvian Man* and Hedden's *Vitruvian Woman* illustrate the divine imprint of the Golden Ratio throughout the form and function of the human body.

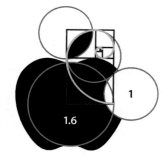

Apple's iconic logo reflects the Golden Ratio as do many Apple products and OS icons. Our graphic analysis overlay reveals 1.6:1 ratios between the Apple's contours, byte and leaf.

Activate Your Unique Genius via Fractal Cognition™

Fractals are found at all scales throughout the Universe and have the remarkable ability to impart knowledge of a whole concept in an instant. Fractals contain the entire array of information in any pattern or object: no matter how many times a pattern or object is divided, the parts or fractals retain the entirety of the original information or structure. For example, in a head of broccoli, each smaller piece (fractal) looks like a miniature version of the whole head. Through Fractal Cognition,™,* vast amounts of knowledge can be conveyed via a tiny piece of that knowledge. By contemplating Nature's ubiquitous fractal patterns—sunflowers, ocean waves, spiral galaxies, etc.—a Eureka! flash of profound insight occurs, unveiling a golden bridge of imagination to the infinite. You realize that the entire Universe is constructed with countless variations on the same Golden Ratio fractal theme. Your brain's latent Golden Ratio genius operating system will thus be activated, just as with countless other geniuses throughout history. *Note: Fractal Cognition™ is a term coined by Matthew Cross; from FRACTAL: A small part which retains the pattern of the whole, as a piece of broccoli retains the pattern of the whole head + COGNITION: To cognate, know, understand.*

Leonardo Da Vinci and Apple use the Golden Ratio

The Golden Ratio endows any creation with a sublime beauty and sense of unity that Da Vinci's mentor Fra Luca Pacioli called Divine Proportion (Pacioli's book on the subject was illustrated by Da Vinci). This is a key reason that Da Vinci's masterpiece, the *Mona Lisa*, continues to conjure such deep fascination five centuries after Da Vinci painted it. It's understandable when you consider that Da Vinci embedded many aspects of the Golden Ratio into his great works. The beautiful and alluring *Mona Lisa* is not the only one who's benefited from Divine Proportion. Apple's world-famous logo also features Golden Ratios in its classically simple, zen-like design. Our analysis confirms that key elements of the logo conform to a ratio of 1.6:1. The Golden Ratio-resonant image of an apple with a *byte* missing innately delights the viewer, as do the numerous Golden Ratios found in the elegant designs of many Apple products. Our brain's built-in software naturally recognizes and is drawn to Divine Proportion, which we sense as beauty and quality, universally attractive and pleasing to all. Nature created the Universe with the Golden Ratio foremost in mind, simultaneously giving us the ability to recognize its timeless beauty and harness its practical application. What a profound, cross-reflecting system!

Yet some of skeptical mind insist that the Golden Ratio is nothing special, at best a random occurrence. Lacking a sense of awe or curiosity, they seem unable to recognize or appreciate its profound ubiquity, utility and beauty. Caging the Golden Ratio within the realm of the ordinary or coincidental limits creativity, exploration and evolution. Like adamant flat-earthers of centuries ago, overly rational left-brained thinking is out-of-ratio in denying the profound implications of the mystical, most irrational number in mathematics: the Golden Ratio/Phi Φ, 1.618... A more open perspective on the Golden Ratio offers anyone applying it in their chosen field greater artistic, scientific and spiritual insight. For those with a more skeptical view on this magnificent mystery, may they broaden their outlook with the help of these sage words from Golden Ratio genius Albert Einstein:

> *The most beautiful thing we can experience is the mysterious. It is the source of all true art and all science. He to whom this emotion is a stranger, who can no longer pause to wonder and stand rapt in awe, is as good as dead: his eyes are closed...*

Elegantly echoing Einstein from across time, Socrates said: *Wisdom begins in wonder.* Obi-Wan Kenobi could easily have been referring to the Golden Ratio when he described The Force to Luke Skywalker in George Lucas' *Star Wars*:

> *It surrounds us, it penetrates us; it binds the galaxy together.*

In this way the Golden Ratio is like air—it's all around us, it infuses us with life, yet most of the time we take it totally for granted—and breathe without thinking. Yet as with the benefits of breathing with awareness and depth, the benefits of appreciating and working with the Golden Ratio, the Pattern of Life, are vast and exponential.

Beyond Measure

The Golden Ratio is Nature's way of expressing the good, the true and the beautiful. The mind of man, through geometry and mathematics, has created formal measures that can accurately identify the Golden Ratio across an infinite variety of Nature's and humanity's creations. With the help of grids, calipers and mathematical proofs we can show to a reasonable degree whether or not something conforms to the Golden Ratio. Yet sometimes the water gets blurry, as when a beautiful face or a transcendent piece of art or music doesn't easily lend itself to formal measurement. Systems of measure fail us at this point, because much of what anyone deems beautiful is due to their status as an observer— a beholder of beauty. Grids, calipers, mathematical proofs and the like become useless when we enter this realm of the immeasurable. Quality genius Dr. W. Edwards Deming observed that the most important things often cannot be measured, e.g.,

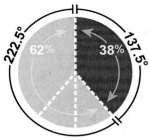

Golden Angles (137.5° & 222.5°) are Golden Ratio evolutionary adaptations seen in the geometry of a plant's optimal leaf and branch distribution (phyllotaxis). These angles are also seen in the peace symbol.

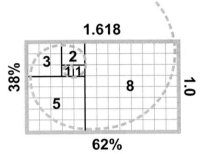

Multiple ways of expressing the Golden Ratio/Phi Φ: as a Golden Rectangle, a Golden Spiral, the Fibonacci Sequence, 62% to 38% and 1.618:1.

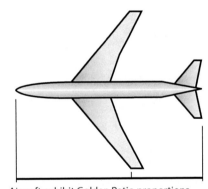

Aircraft exhibit Golden Ratio proportions in their design and structure, to maximize lift and minimize drag.

Lexus offers one of countless elegant examples of Golden Ratio resonance and aesthetics in fine product design.

The immune system boosting Echinacea flower, beautifully displaying the Golden Spiral Pattern of Life.

Most every flag the world over flies in the shape of the Golden Rectangle. Many also contain Golden Stars.

Great Seal of the United States of America, a study in hidden-in-plain-sight Golden Ratios by master geometer Michael S. Schneider. Note the eight Golden Rectangles of four different sizes revealed in Schneider's study.

The star pentagram is one of the most recognized, classic icons of the Golden Ratio. That it also stands for greatness, quality, power, love, wisdom and health is fitting.

love or beauty. Therein lies a Divine paradox: while we may not always be able to measure the presence of the Golden Ratio in a person or thing, we can invite it into our creations and endeavors through conscious awareness and design, a process that can benefit from the utilization of simple tools, techniques and measures. When objective measurements fail, we can take comfort in knowing that our brains are also accurate meters of Divine Proportion, since they too are anatomically and physiologically designed according to the Golden Ratio; it takes one to know one. This book challenges you to understand the Golden Ratio from both perspectives, that of mathematical and geometrical rigor and also from the subjective viewpoint, from the lofty perspective of your naturally innate sense of Divine Proportion.

The Golden Key to Success in Every Measure

The ancients used the Golden Ratio in their art and architecture to bring the essence of Nature into their designs and culture. Beautiful medieval churches are a classic example of how use of this Nature principle resulted in awe-inspiring places of worship, communion and spirit. Much of so-called modern architecture shows an utter lack of attunement with Nature that could be otherwise attained by aligning with the Golden Ratio. We can achieve a restoration of Nature—and thus ourselves—by incorporating Golden Ratio elements in not just our art and architecture, but in any human endeavor and life facet. As with our health, relationships and success in life, our connection to Nature and one another can be restored and invigorated through simple application of the Golden Ratio. If a critical mass of individuals likewise awakens to their genius potential, we may experience a renaissance of life, liberty and the enjoyment of greater happiness, beauty and success in every measure.

As you journey through this book, you'll discover how Nature and humanity manifest beauty, efficiency and success through the Golden Ratio. This is the Golden Key we've carried with us since our journey began in our mother's womb. Once you begin to grasp the essence of the Golden Ratio, you'll start to naturally "connect the dots" and your unique genius will activate and grow. Then, when you integrate the Golden Ratio into your life and work in any way, you'll be able to predict with higher certainty more innovative, creative and successful results. In addition, a renewed sense of inner and outer connection with the Divine will naturally emerge—what Einstein colleague David Bohm termed implicate and explicate order. The implicate order is what is within each and every one of us, including our Golden Ratio coded anatomical and physiological functioning, our mental processes, emotions and behaviors. The flip side of the Divine coin, the explicate order, is what we see in the Golden Ratio structured world around us, at every scale throughout Nature and the cosmos.

This book is a primer, a portal to the infinite world of the Golden Ratio. Humanity's unending search for it is as infinite and unending as the Ratio itself. Due to its purity, synergizing action, uncanny ubiquity and universal value, the Golden Ratio may well be the underlying blueprint of the universal unified field. The Golden Ratio is of such all-encompassing magnitude it is truly worthy of being considered a theory of everything, perhaps even a universal law. As Albert Einstein said,

> A theory [e.g., the Golden Ratio] is more impressive, the greater the simplicity of its premise, the more different the kinds of things it relates and the more extended its range of applicability.

The Golden Ratio and Fibonacci Sequence are your Golden Keys to genius, health, wealth and excellence. Overlooked by many, recognized as the Golden Grail by a few, this profound knowledge has the potential to ignite your unique genius, greatness and mission. It's an invitation to begin a journey of discovery and realization of your deep interconnectedness with the source code of life and structure of the Universe. *To Infinity and Beyond!*

Editor's Note: Only a few Golden Ratio elements are illustrated on select pictures throughout this book with either Golden Ratio line graphs, Golden Ratio calipers or PhiMatrix™ grids.

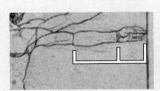

The remainder of the pictures are presented without graphs, calipers or grids to both keep the presentation simple and uncluttered and to allow you to discover for yourself the many Golden Ratios present yet not identified.

For more in-depth study of the Golden Ratio's ubiquity and practical applications to health, learning, success and life, see the authors' other books: The Golden Ratio Lifestyle Diet • The Divine Code of Da Vinci, Fibonacci, Einstein & YOU • The Millionaire's MAP • The Genius Activation Quote Book.

The Golden Ratio is found in structures ancient and modern around the globe, from the Great Pyramid to Notre Dame to the Empire State Building.

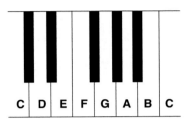

C D E F G A B C

5 Black Keys
8 White Keys
13 Keys Span 1 Octave

Ebony & Ivory: Golden Ratio construction harmony of musical instruments follows Fibonacci intervals, as seen on a piano's keyboard: 1 octave spans 13 keys, 8 white keys, 5 black keys in groups of 3 & 2. Natural harmonics of musical tones also follow Fibonacci intervals. The Music of the Spheres comes to life through instruments designed according to the Divine pattern of beauty and harmony.

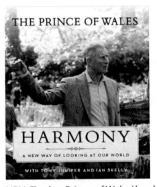

HRH Charles, Prince of Wales' book *Harmony: A New Way Of Looking At The World* explores the Golden Ratio, Fibonacci Sequence and sacred geometry's role in the restoration of the human spirit and the planet: *Harmony* exposes how the patterns of the natural world, which for centuries were woven into the fabric of human life, have been lost in the modern age. The Prince is an eloquent ambassador for the cultural renaissance of the wisdom encoded in the sacred Patterns of Life.

0

The Golden Ratio is the secret of the Universe.

Pythagoras

Galactic & Planetary

There is music in the spacing of the spheres, said the great mathematician Pythagoras, in his sage description of the Universe. Long intuited by visionary geniuses over time, it is only since the perfection of modern telescopes that the Golden Ratio is seen to extend into infinity—and beyond. From great galaxies swirling in Golden Spiral trails of stars to the spacing of planets in our solar system to the weather systems and ocean waves on Earth, we see a Universe vibrantly alive with the master design code.

Plato's unified field theory conjectured that the Universe was made up of 5 basic shapes known as the Platonic solids: tetrahedron, octahedron, cube, icosahedron and dodecahedron. Platonic shapes increase their ability to encompass a sphere as they shift from tetrahedron to dodecahedron, a 3-D way of squaring the circle. Many other geniuses followed Plato's lead, including Johannes Kepler, formulator of the laws of planetary motion. Kepler was among the early pioneers who realized that the Golden Ratio is a golden key to understanding the cosmos' design symmetry and unity. The shape of the entire Universe is now theorized to resemble a dodecahedron, a 12-sided volume bounded by Golden Ratio pentagons. Quantum Physicist Max Planck's "Planck Length" (1.62×10^{-35m}) is postulated to be a multiple of the Ratio, measuring the width of a wormhole in space. The golden blueprint guiding the placement and movement of heavenly bodies fires the imagination. Indeed, Albert Einstein was inspired as a boy by the Fibonacci Sequence's prevalence in the grand design to seek and ultimately reach into the infinity of space and time, expanding forever our view of the Golden Ratio-patterned Universe.

Great golden galaxy spirals reflect the master design principle of the Universe at the macro end of the scale. Pictured is Galaxy M-74.

Soccer balls are ubiquitous reminders of both the theorized shape of the Universe and its Golden Ratio-rich building blocks, called Buckminsterfullerenes or "BuckyBalls."

In the heavens as on Earth, Golden Rectangles can be found. Galaxy LEDA, discovered in 2012, fits neatly inside a Golden Rectangle.

Like Plato, Johannes Kepler postulated the Golden Ratio harmony of the Universe. His model of planetary orbits shows each nested Platonic solid 1.618 x the next.

The Sun's magnetic field assumes a great 3-D Golden Spiral as it extends through the solar system, a.k.a. the Parker Spiral/heliospheric current sheet.

The Golden Ratio-based icosahedron has 20 triangular faces forming 12 pentagons. Buckminster Fuller used it as the basis for his geodesic dome and Dymaxion Map.

Hurricanes are huge Golden Spiral vortexes of wind and water, utilizing Nature's Path of Least Resistance to generate and release their vast energies.

Earth & Moon in Golden Ratio: A triangle with Phi relationships forms between them, based on their relative radii; relationships also seen in the Great Pyramid's design.

Buckminster Fuller's Dymaxion World Map unfolds from a Golden Ratio-based icosahedron, whose triangles unify the continents into one contiguous island in one ocean.

Platonic solids are 5 archetypal universal building blocks. The Golden Ratio-based icosahedron (purple) and dodecahedron (blue) can approximate a sphere.

In our solar system, the "Music of the Spheres" is evident in the Golden Ratio relationships between planets.

Viewed from Earth, Venus' orbit around the sun scribes Golden Pentagonal flowers and heart shapes. Venus orbits the Sun 13 times for every 8 Earth orbits, a Fibonacci Ratio.

The latitudes of the Tropics of Cancer and Capricorn approximate the Golden Ratio, when measured from the Equator in relation to the poles.

18

Φ 1.618
√Φ
1.0

COSMOGRAPHICUM

1.0   1.618

MERCURY   VENUS   EARTH   MARS

0° E or W
Arctic

23.5° N   23.5° N
TROPIC OF
CANCER
0° N or S   EQUATOR   0° N or S
23.5° S   TROPIC OF   23.5° S
CAPRICORN

North   North   Europe   Asia   North
America   Atlantic   Pacific
Middle
East
Central   Caribbean   Africa
America
South   Oceania   Indian
America
South   Australia
Pacific   South
Atlantic

Antarctica

PRIME
MERIDIAN

1a

The Golden Ratio is the Pattern of Life.
John Michell

Nature

At every scale, Nature delights in moving and growing with the Golden Ratio. From the movement of the elements, from water to wind to fire to earth, through all life, we see the Golden Ratio and Fibonacci Sequence at work and play. From the Spiral motion of hurricanes and ocean waves, to the geometric growth patterns of sea shells and starfish, the Pattern of Life is infinitely abundant. Mother Nature's ubiquitous use of the Golden Ratio and Fibonacci Sequence as a central architectural code serves as the mysteriously delightful repeating theme throughout inanimate and animate life, in land, sea and air.

Honeybees are an intriguing example of the multiplexed manifestations of the grand pattern: bee bodies segmented in Golden Ratio, flight patterns mirroring Golden Spirals and idealized genealogy and navigation through their hives mirroring the Fibonacci Sequence. Plant growth in turn is guided by the pattern: precise stalk branching and leaf placement for optimal sun exposure (phyllotaxis); flowers with seeds in Golden Spirals for most efficient packing and petals tuned to Fibonacci Sequence numbers, and fruit in Golden Ratio design and Golden Star seed cores, e.g., apples. From pinecones to cheetah claws, elephant trunks to fin placement on dolphins, the endless symphony of the Pattern of Life reveals the sublime Golden Ratio artistry of Mother Nature. As visionary inventor Nikola Tesla said, *Every living being is an engine geared to the wheelwork of the Universe.*

Sunflowers encode multiple Golden Ratios, from elegant Golden Spiral seed placement, Fibonacci Numbers of petals to Golden Ratios of petals-to-face radii.

Phyllotaxis is the growth and arrangement of stems, leaves, flowers and seeds for optimal sun, air and rain exposure. This pattern encodes the Fibonacci Sequence.

Plant growth follows the Fibonacci Sequence for optimal efficiency, as seen in this side-on view of phyllotaxis.

Many trees fit neatly inside a Golden Rectangle (facing page), with branches and leaves corresponding to the Fibonacci Sequence and ratios respectively.

Golden Ratio function follows Golden Ratio form. Bees' flight patterns and body structure mirror the master design code replicated throughout Nature at all scales.

Hummingbirds exhibit enchanting Golden Ratio proportions, which naturally optimizes their legendary quickness and hovering capabilities.

The multidirectional spirals formed by the scales on pineapples are in Fibonacci Ratio. Depending on the pineapple, there can be either 5, 8 & 13 spirals or 8, 13 & 21 spirals.

Dogs, like all of Nature's creatures, are imprinted with Golden Ratio form and function. Snakes, snails, cat claws and puppy dog tails reflect this cosmic design.

Apple blossoms are beautiful Golden Stars, reflecting the ubiquitous, dynamic pattern of life found throughout Nature.

The Golden Star seed pattern at every apple's core mirrors the same pattern as the blossoms from which they grow; Divine intelligence at work.

Pinecones exhibit Golden Ratios and the Fibonacci Sequence in their spirals and numbers of modified leaves; pine trees' outlines often describe a Golden Rectangle.

The iconic Nautilus shell is a graceful logarithmic spiral and although not a Golden Spiral, exhibits exquisite Golden Ratio harmonics in its design.

Every bee's multiple path choices through their honeycombs mysteriously follow the Fibonacci Sequence, as does their genealogy. Protect the Bees: Ban Pesticides & GMOs.

The graceful Golden Ratio hydrodynamics of a dolphin's body. Marine and land animals alike embody the Golden Ratio in their body's structure and movement.

Starfish are literally living pentagrams, key archetypes of the Golden Ratio. Curiously, they also possess the power to miraculously regenerate any lost "star legs."

Ocean waves crash continuously on every shore on Earth; countless Golden Spiral waves of every size follow Nature's Path of Least Resistance in an endless symphony.

1b

*To see a world in a grain of sand, and a heaven
in a wildflower, hold infinity in the palm of
your hand, and eternity in an hour.*

William Blake

MicroWorlds

As above, so below is a fitting description for the ubiquitous appearance of the Golden Ratio and Fibonacci Sequence at every scale. This phenomenon is the ultimate example of the fractal principle, where an identical pattern is repeated from the macro to the micro, also known as self-similarity. It should thus come as no surprise that atoms can be observed dancing in the same Golden Spirals as galaxies, or that the proportions of microscopic diatoms, quasicrystals and Penrose tiles exhibit Golden Ratios in their structures or that DNA—the Code of Life—mirrors it in its dimensions.

R. Buckminster Fuller's geodesic domes foretold by decades the discovery of sixty-carbon-atom (C-60) spherical molecules called Buckminsterfullerenes or "Buckyballs." Scientists Kroto, Smalley and Curl expanded on Fuller's genius insights and work, winning the 1996 Nobel Prize in chemistry for their actual discovery of Buckyballs. These soccer-ball-shaped molecules named in Fuller's honor are composed of 12 pentagons and 20 hexagons and are replete with Golden Ratio geometry. The applications of these super molecules appear endless and are further evidence of Golden Ratio geometry being found throughout the Universe at every scale. The timeless beauty of the poet Kahlil Gibran's words come to mind: *I discovered the secret of the sea in meditation upon a dew drop.*

Nature's grand design template is evident even at the atomic level, where atoms in an atomic bubble chamber trace the same beautiful Golden Spirals as galaxies.

Electron micrograph of a nano-gold particle with icosahedral Golden Ratio geometry. One of the 5 Platonic solids, it is a template underlying crystals and microrganisms.

A diatom exhibiting the Pattern of Life as a Golden Star. Diatoms are microscopic, uni-cellular algae organisms of many geometric shapes found in oceans, water and earth.

Quasicrystals are unique microstructures with multiple Golden Ratio design elements. Their discovery led to a 2011 Nobel Prize for scientist Dan Shechtman.

Magnified xylitol crystal, showing pentagonal structure. A medicinal natural sugar substitute, it neutralizes tooth decay causing bacteria and promotes oral health.

Viewed from above, the DNA molecule resembles a sacred mandala, revealing a beautiful decagonal pattern which is based on Golden Ratio geometry.

The Buckminsterfullerene or "Buckyball" is one of Nature's premier Golden Ratio molecular building blocks, with elegantly integrated pentagons and hexagons.

To see a world in a grain of sand… Sublime examples of Nature's spiral and pentagonal geometry in grains of common sand, via the microphotography of Dr. Gary Greenberg.

2

Man is the measure of all things.
Protagoras

Humanity

We carry the golden key to the Universe in our hands, literally. Each of our finger bones, from smallest to largest, is in approximate Golden Ratio to its neighbor, a phenomenon repeated in our hand-to-forearm ratio. This marvelous linear connectivity to the unity code of the Universe animates into a graceful Golden Spiral with each movement—every time we curl and uncurl our fingers, hands and limbs we trace the same spiral as a galaxy, ocean wave or the pattern of seeds on a sunflower's face.

In the structure and movement of everything within the sacred temple of our bodies, from our DNA all the way up to the proportion of our body's upper and lower sections, we are living testaments of the Golden Ratio. It elegantly unites us—all of our parts to one another, one person to every other and to all life. Even the ratio of our emotions, of expansive or positive thoughts to contractive or negative thoughts mirrors the Golden Ratio, averaging 62% positive to 38% negative, as revealed in the research of Dr. Vladimir Lefebvre. All of our biorhythms, including our breathing, heartbeat, sleep and nutrition are magically guided and optimized by the Pattern of Life. All that makes us human at every stage, from embryo to fetus to child to adult, including our communication, emotions, relationships and intimacy is guided by the Ratio. We grow and mature in natural accordance with it; as we'll see ahead, our bodies, health and lifespan—and our innate genius—thrive with attunement to it. The Pattern of Life is simply yet profoundly the pattern of our highest expression and potential as human beings.

The human eye exhibits multiple embedded Golden Ratio proportions in its structure and facial feature relationships. Note similarity to the CBS "eye" logo.

The human brain is designed with Divine Proportion in mind. Brainwave frequencies and ratios of positive to negative emotions (62% to 38%) also mirror the Golden Ratio.

The fetal-shaped human ear follows a Golden Spiral. This structural design facilitates the optimal focusing of sound waves.

The Golden Spiral hair growth pattern at the top of everyone's head is evidence of the amazing guiding forces at work throughout the human body's design.

All humans begin life's journey unfolding in a gentle Golden Spiral, whose imprint continues throughout our lives in our form, function, thinking and feeling patterns.

A beautiful smile reflects teeth in Golden Ratio. Restorative dentists like Beverly Hills' Dr. David Frey enhance beauty, functionality and health with this knowledge.

The Golden Ratio's unity pattern is found throughout humanity's structure, movement and community, reminding us of our interconnectedness with all creation.

Composite of *Vitruvian Man* by Leonardo Da Vinci and *Vitruvian Woman* by Chloe Hedden; handsome Golden Ratio archetypes of idealized humans in Divine Proportion.

DNA reveals Nature's sacred life geometry. The double helix's length-to-width helical structure is in Golden Ratio. The Pattern of Life thus blueprints the Divine Code of Life.

Not only is DNA's length/width ratio 1.618:1, Jean-Claude Perez, Ph.D., proved that DNA's building blocks (G,C,T,A) are fractally structured according to the Golden Ratio.

The bones in our body are in Golden Ratio to one another. The grid in this illustration delineates how the forearm is in Golden Ratio to the hand and fingers.

The human heart generates its contractive force via a synergy of structure and function; its spiral-shaped muscles contract in a Golden Spiral-like motion in every beat.

A healthy heart's Electrocardiogram (ECG): ratios of contraction and relaxation are in Golden Ratio. Another profound example of Golden Ratio function and form at work.

Contrary to popular belief, the human heart sits not in the center of the chest, but left-of-center, residing at the Golden Ratio division between left and right sides.

As above, so below. Trees' fractal branching and root patterns mirror lung's bronchial branching patterns. In an interdependent dance, our lungs & trees exchange O_2 & CO_2.

Breath is the #1 driver of health and longevity. Deep breathing with a 3 to 5 second inhalation/exhalation Fibonacci ratio increases oxygen uptake and vitality.

Our lungs display many Fibonacci and Golden Ratios in their multiple bronchial segment lengths, down to the alveolar fractal level. Also, 2 L lobes and 3 R lobes.

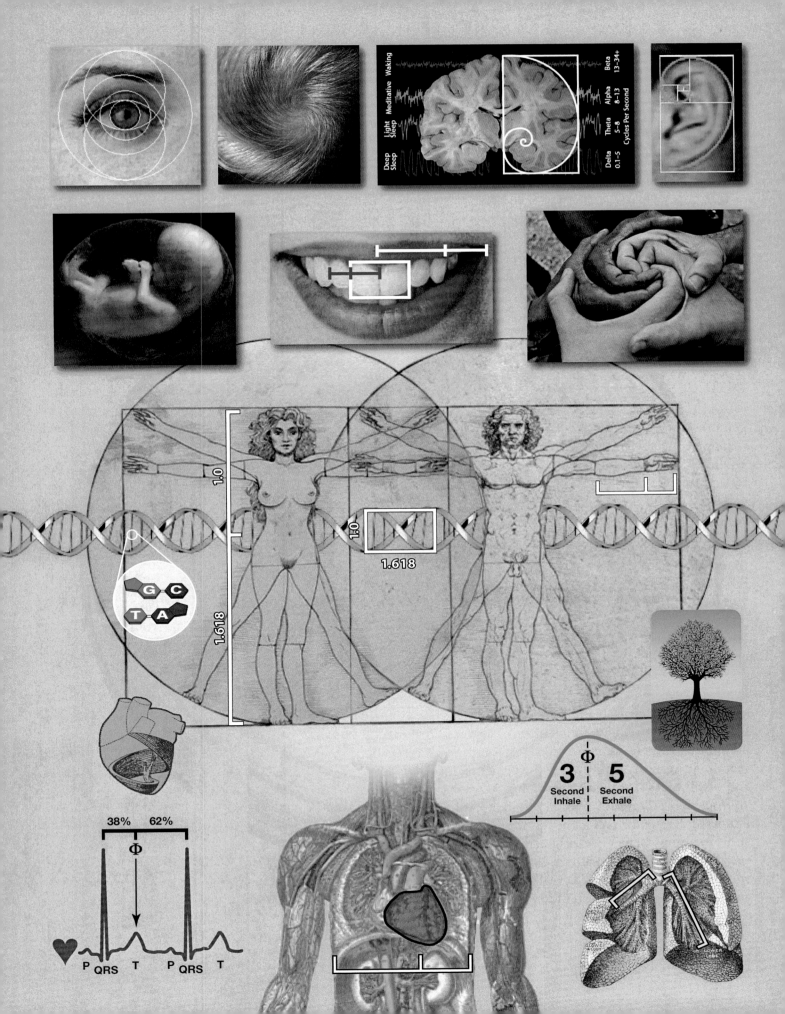

The Golden Ratio has inspired thinkers of all disciplines like no other number in the history of mathematics.

Mario Livio

Geniuses & Culture Shifters

Since the beginning of recorded

history a luminous, golden thread has connected countless geniuses and culture shifters. Known by many names down through the ages—Golden Ratio, Golden Mean or Section, Divine Proportion, Phi Φ, Tau τ—the principle is one; a rose by any other name. Whether consciously or unconsciously accessed and applied, the genius of the Golden Ratio can be seen in the timeless works of illuminated thinkers, dreamers and doers to the present day.

Many geniuses such as Pythagoras, Plato, Euclid, Leonardo Fibonacci, Descartes, Apple's Steve Wozniak, Nobel Prize winners Albert Einstein and Murray Gell-Mann and business mogul Anastasia Soare spoke openly about their fascination with and inspiration from the Golden Ratio and/ or Fibonacci Sequence. Others, like Leonardo Da Vinci, Thomas Jefferson, Frank Lloyd Wright, Karl Pribram, the Beatles, Steve Jobs and Michael Jackson revealed it clearly and repeatedly in their culture-shifting work. The Golden Ratio is a master catalyst which inspires genius and pervades its infinite, unique manifestations. All geniuses exhibit the seemingly uncanny ability to see the bigger picture or pattern and distill their vision and inspiration in ways that advance and quicken cultural evolution. Contemplating the infinite Fibonacci Sequence is a great reminder to *Dream Bigger*— and Dreaming Bigger was sage advice from Golden Ratio genius Steve Jobs. The Pattern of Life is also the pattern of enlightenment, offering us a great golden switch to ignite our genius and imagination and illuminate the world.

Leonardo Da Vinci imprinted the Golden Ratio throughout his timeless body of work. The quintessential Renaissance Man, his genius continues to impact our world.

Albert Einstein's discovery of the Fibonacci Sequence at age 13 unleashed his world-transforming genius: *The Divine Proportion… makes the bad difficult and the good easy.*

The Greek philosopher Plato described the Platonic solid shapes, the building blocks of our Universe. He considered the Golden Ratio to be the key to the cosmos.

Hildegard von Bingen, legendary German monastic leader, mystic and composer, whose sacred musical compositions are richly infused with the Golden Ratio.

Euclid wrote of the Golden Ratio: *A straight line is said to have been cut in extreme and mean ratio when, as the whole line is to the greater segment, so is the greater to the lesser.*

Leonardo Fibonacci introduced Hindu/ Arabic numerals, the decimal (.) and zer0 to the West in the 1200's and (via the Rabbit Riddle) the Fibonacci Sequence 0,1,1,2,3,5…

Ancient Greek mathematician Pythagoras is credited with the extreme and mean ratio concept of the Golden Mean. His secret society's sign was the pentagram.

Johannes Kepler expounded the laws of planetary motion and was fascinated by the Golden Ratio, calling it *Geometry's Most Precious Jewel.*

Jonathan Ive is Apple Inc.'s lead designer whose cutting edge creations enhance the human technological interface while showcasing exquisite Golden Ratio artistry.

Steve Wozniak, co-founder of Apple Inc., was inspired by the Fibonacci Sequence and is renowned for the elegant simplicity of his hardware and software designs.

Thomas Jefferson, 3rd American President, polymath and Declaration of Independence author, designed the Golden Ratio-replete University of Virginia Rotunda.

Frank Lloyd Wright used the fractal principle of the Golden Ratio in his classic architectural designs, embedding the ratio over a wide range of scales.

R. Buckminster Fuller inspired the discovery of the Buckminsterfullerene or BuckyBall, a Golden Ratio-rich molecule and Universal building block with infinite applications.

Walt Disney's *Donald in Mathmagic Land* (1959) and classic motto, *When you wish upon a Star, your dreams come true…* transmit the Golden Ratio's infinite magic.

Golden Ratio genius geometer John Michell exemplified Socrates' wisdom: *There is a pattern in the heavens; those who want to can establish it in their hearts.*

Ralph N. Elliott's pattern recognition epiphany led to the Elliott Wave Theory of stock market movement, based on social moods expressed via Fibonacci and Golden Ratios.

Anastasia Soare transformed the field of facial aesthetics and natural beauty by ingeniously shaping eyebrows with Golden Ratio proportion to enhance facial beauty.

Apple Inc. co-founder Steve Jobs revolutionized the world with Golden Ratio imprinted products that empower and inspire people to express their creative genius.

5

The Golden Ratio is Nature's universal thread, with which optimal health is woven.

Robert Friedman, M.D. and Matthew Cross

Health & Longevity

What if the Fountain of Youth

existed right within our bodies, programmed into our DNA? How might we access this golden key to greater quality and quantity of life? Like a super-vitamin which never expires and works for everyone, regardless of age or condition, restoring the Golden Ratio in our lives helps to restore the body to its original, divine blueprint of health and optimal longevity. This is Nature's Secret Nutrient (NSN) or "Vitamin Phi" in action.

Starting with the Divine geometric proportions of our DNA, as we move up the scale of our body's systems and structures we find that all function more optimally when better attuned to the Golden Ratio. This supports a state of heightened synergy, where the whole exceeds the sum of its parts. The closer our key health and longevity drivers reflect the Ratio, the longer we can expect to live a higher quality life. These prioritized drivers include our breathing, hydration, sleep, nutrition, posture, exercise and detoxification. As with all living things, when you're aligned closer to the Ratio, greater harmony and efficiency of form and function are natural results—along with enhanced beauty, vigor and lifespan. Happiness, gratitude and inner peace also grow accordingly. This is the powerful potential which can result from complimenting your health and lifestyle regimen with Nature's Secret Nutrient: the Golden Ratio.

Sunlight's UVA and UVB wavelengths are in Golden Ratio. One of Nature's Secret Nutrients for optimal health, it's a natural source of immune system booster Vitamin D.

Happiness is derived 60% by genetics/life circumstances, 40% by behavior/thoughts. Research indicates the genetic side is greatly expandable via positive lifestyle choices.

A Golden Ratio of about 15 hours awake to 9 hours total of sleep *or* rest is ideal for optimal health, performance and longevity. Lack of ample sleep shortens life.

A 40/30/30 (i.e. 40/60) carbs/protein/fat ratio is a near optimal Golden Ratio Zone range of macronutrients; enhances total health and keeps inflammation at bay.

Vital Capacity, the total amount of air exhaled after a full breath, is the #1 predictor of longevity. Golden Ratio breathing techniques can greatly enhance your Vital Capacity.

The Golden Ratio Lifestyle Diet offers new techniques to slow down and potentially reverse the aging process. Note that the true definition of *Diet* is actually *Lifestyle*.

Restoring the Golden Ratio in our primary health drivers strengthens our immune system's PacMan®-like defense capabilities, protecting us from toxins and disease.

Dan Buettner's Blue Zone longevity research is Golden Ratio Lifestyle resonant: ample water and rest, smaller meals, active lifestyle, strong life purpose/faith/network, red wine, etc.

A healthy Golden Ratio balance of Omega-3 to Omega-6 fats is vital for optimum cellular health and reduced inflammation; fish oil + flax seeds support often deficient Omega-3s.

By using Fibonacci Ratios (e.g., 5 to 3) of exercise to rest, the Golden Ratio Workout Wave increases energy and performance, while reducing injuries and overtraining.

Da Vinci's ideal human, the *Vitruvian Man*, has a Golden Ratio body water percentage of about 62%. Urine color of chardonnay or lighter helps assess healthy hydration.

Digestion is most efficient when your stomach is no more than 62% full. This Golden Ratio full point is about equal to the volume of food fitting in both hands lightly cupped together.

Buoyant posture, standing or sitting, restores Golden Ratio relationships between your vertebrae, improves breathing, bioelectric flow and decompresses organs.

Dr. Hanno Ulmer discovered that blood pressure in well people exhibits a Golden systolic/diastolic ratio of 1.618:1, e.g., 120/75, with increased death risk for those out-of-Ratio.

When your Cholesterol/LDL ratio is in the Golden Ratio range of 1.618:1 (or more simply 62% to 38%), greater health and longevity are natural results.

The Golden Ratio Lifestyle Diet's prioritized 40/30/30 Foundation-Actions-Results™ (FAR) success drivers support robust health, happiness and longevity.

The Fountain of Youth, by German painter Lucas Cranach (1546). *The Golden Ratio Lifestyle Diet* is your golden ticket to your own fountain of youth. Great health to you!

Happiness
- 40% Behavior/Thoughts
- 60% Genetics + Life Circumstances

Nutrition
- 40% Carbs
- 30% Protein
- 30% Fat

Sleep
- 15 Hours Awake
- 9 Hours Sleep/Rest

OMEGA-3

5 5 3

62%

62%

Φ

Total Cholesterol Φ LDL
1.618 1.0

Cervical
Thoracic
Lumbar
Sacral
Coccygeal

Sardinia Abkhazia Hunza
Loma Linda Ikaria
Costa Rica Okinawa
Vilcabamba

40% Foundation → 30% Actions → 30% Results

10	VIBRANT HEALTH & LONGEVITY
9	NATURAL BEAUTY & ATTRACTION
8	HAPPINESS & INNER PEACE
7	DETOXIFICATION
6	EXERCISE
5	POSTURE
4	NUTRITION
3	SLEEP/REST
2	WATER
1	AIR

Beauty is not perfection.
Real beauty is proportion.
   Anastasia Soare

Beauty

Nature in all her forms offers countless examples of breathtaking beauty, the visible language of the Golden Ratio. Whenever beauty is seen, heard or felt, a delightful sense of inspiration and oneness arises. We feel a magical resonance, as if we are somehow united with the beauty before us in a synergistic dance. Invariably we find the Ratio at play in great works of beauty, whether created by man or Nature. Divine Proportions of the parts form a greater whole, which pleasingly exceeds the sum of its parts. The effect is unavoidably magnetic and uplifting.

Beauty reminds us that we are both in the presence of the Divine and also part of it—that the perceiver and the perceived are essentially One. The Golden Ratio of beauty effortlessly unifies the observer and the observed. As in the endless varieties of the exquisite rose, the human face can be the pinnacle of Golden Ratio beauty. Each face is a godly palate where the parts sublimely combine to form a breathtaking expression of Divinity. This phenomenon has been explored throughout the ages and in the work of modern beauty researchers and pioneers such as Anastasia Soare, the first to apply Divine Proportion to universal natural beauty enhancement, via her breakthrough Golden Ratio eyebrow sculpting method; clients include Oprah Winfrey, Jennifer Lopez and Madonna. Along with Anastasia, biostatistics professor Dr. Kendra Schmid's Golden Ratio facial beauty measurement work has also been featured on *Oprah*. While some are graced with an abundance of symmetry and natural beauty, we can all invite more Divine Proportion into our lives by attuning to this universal principle. We can awaken our delight to the inherent Golden Ratio beauty which we all naturally carry and reflect to the world.

George Clooney's universally renowned chiseled good looks place him squarely in the Golden Ratio pantheon of ideally attractive male faces.

The face of every rose reveals petals arranged in multiple beautiful Golden Spiral patterns as part of its double Golden Ratio imprint.

The back of every rose reveals a 5-pointed Golden Star as part of its double Golden Ratio imprint, true to its ancient roots as the guiding star of the compass rose.

In addition to her natural self-taught talent, is Jennifer Lawrence's universal, Oscar®-winning allure also due in part to her beautiful Golden Ratio proportions?

Marilyn Monroe's timeless popularity is clearly due to her Divinely Proportioned shape, endearing personality and charisma.

Actress and model Monica Dean is a classic example of universal attractiveness, being endowed with a beautifully proportioned face and appearance.

Sean Connery, the ultimate, suave and debonair Bond... James Bond. *People* magazine's *Sexiest Man of the Century* personifies the Golden Ratio in style.

Jennifer Lopez's beautiful facial features are enhanced by Anastasia of Beverly Hills' Golden Ratio eyebrow sculpting system; other clients include Oprah and Madonna.

Like Da Vinci's two-dimensional *Vitruvian Man*, Michelangelo's three-dimensional sculpture *David* exhibits the archetypal Golden Ratio proportions of the ideal man.

Venus de Milo is a classic example of how ancient artisans used the Golden Ratio in sculpture to express the timeless ideals of balance, beauty and symmetry.

13

The lover is drawn by the thing loved,
as the sense is by that which it perceives.

Leonardo Da Vinci

Love & Connection

The universal archetype of love is the idealized shape of the human heart. Two Golden Spirals reveal a beautiful heart only when they are in harmonious relationship to one another. This idea can also apply to time and space ratios in healthy relationships, e.g., 62% together, 38% apart. Kahlil Gibran expressed this spirit in *The Prophet: Let there be spaces in your togetherness, and let the winds of the heavens dance between you...*

The planet Venus has symbolized love and beauty for millennia, a fact linked to its heavenly Golden Ratio dance. Venus orbits the Sun 13 times for every 8 Earth orbits (13:8 is a Fibonacci Ratio), in the process scribing exquisite starflower and heart-shaped designs in the heavens. The Greeks and Romans marveled at the planet's celestial dance, infusing their Goddesses Aphrodite and Venus with the Divine qualities of love and beauty. This was one way the Ratio was woven into their cultures, an imprint which continues to this day. From the Golden Ratios found within our key communication channels (body language, words, voice tone), to those present within our communication modalities (visual, auditory, kinesthetic), greater love, beauty and harmony abound in our universe when these ratios reflect Divine balance. The Golden Ratio underscores the true aim of communication, hidden within the word's Latin origins: Comm = Come Together; Uni = One. Communication = *to come together as one.* One heart, one mind, one spirit out of two or more. When communication quality and quantity is in healthy proportion, connecting and creating a greater whole—the Golden Ratio function in action—is a natural result.

Two Golden Spirals reveal a beautiful heart when the spirals are positioned in harmonious relationship to one another—not too close, yet not too far.

Natural heart of Golden Spirals formed by the loving communion of two swans. Nature delights in reminding us of her infinitely Divine patterns of life and love.

Chocolate is one of Nature's ultimate aphrodisiacs, genius superfood and potent antioxidant, with a 62:38 Golden Ratio of saturated to unsaturated fat. Dark is Divine!

Cocoa beans, chocolate's precursor, grow in a pentagonal Golden Ratio pattern. Legend says chocolate is a gift of the Gods; it is also a favorite of many Nobel Prize winners.

The Golden Ratio of Character & Charisma provides a strong foundation for sincere attraction and healthy relationships, as articulated by entrepreneur and writer Jackie Summers.

The Divine Proportion-based Fashion Code enhances any wardrobe. This ingenious method optimizes appearance, increasing one's chances for connection, love and success.

Dynamic relationships dance in an endless Golden Ratio flow between each partner's lead role; giving/receiving, active/passive, leading/following, talking/listening.

Venus orbits the Sun 13 times for every 8 Earth solar orbits (13:8 is a Fibonacci Ratio) and in the process scribes exquisite Golden Ratio starflower and heart-shaped designs.

The population dominance of the primary modes of communication is near Golden Ratio: 60% visual, 20% auditory + 20% kinesthetic (60/40).

Our primary channels of communication are in Golden Ratio: 62% body language and words to 38% voice tone (55% body language + 7% words = 62%).

Our Golden Proportioned hands as well as many seashells naturally form the familiar shape of a heart composed of double Golden Spirals.

The Romans marveled at Venus' celestial dance, infusing their Goddess Venus with the timeless Golden Ratio qualities of love and beauty, which echo to this day.

Bleeding heart flowers exhibit exquisite double Golden Spirals uniting to form a greater whole.

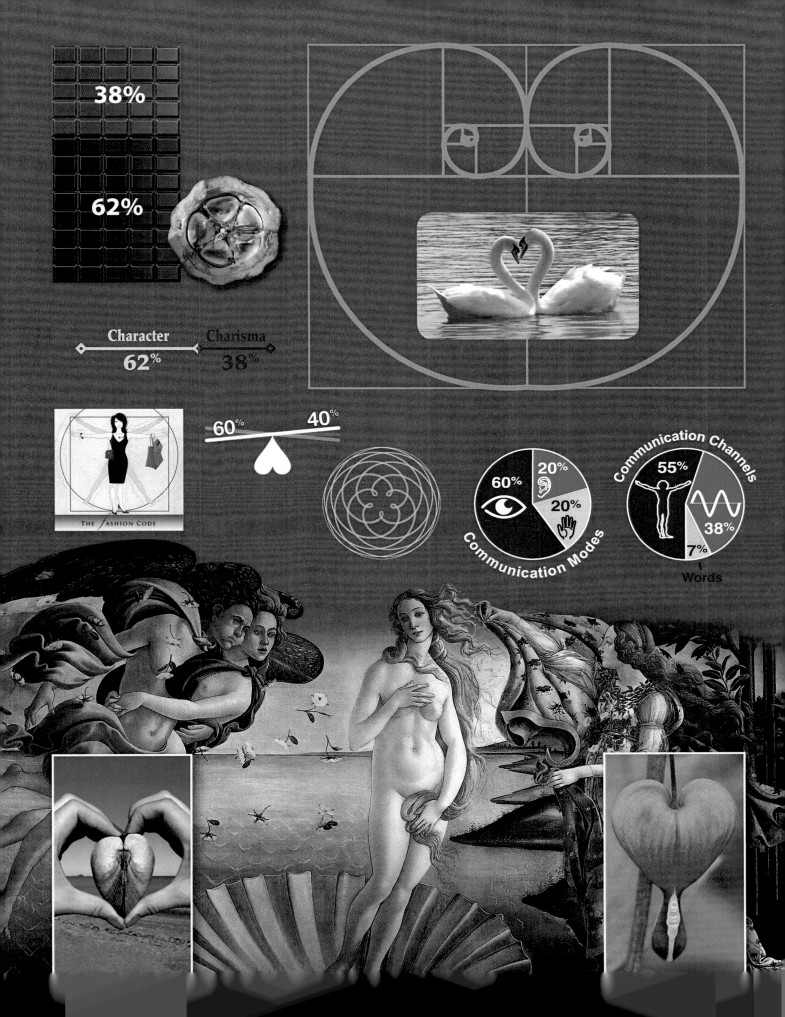

38%

62%

Character 62%   Charisma 38%

The Fashion Code

60%   40%

60%   20%
20%
Communication Modes

Communication Channels
55%   38%
7%
Words

21

Nature's path of least resistance and maximum performance follow the Golden Ratio.

Dr. Ronald Sandler

Peak Performance

Biomimicry is the art and science of imitating brilliant natural designs for human use. We can likewise fine-tune our perception to discover the Golden Ratio in Nature and apply it to human endeavors. In any performance arena, from exercise—recreational or competitive—to work, this can pay huge dividends. Peak performance can be planned with high accuracy when we apply the complimentary laws of rest and activity, which occur in predictable waves. These waves conform to the Golden Ratio and can be activated via the Fibonacci Sequence, allowing anyone at anytime to align activities with Nature's Path of Least Resistance and Maximum Performance.

This insight was first validated by Dr. Ronald Sandler, who discovered that peak performances are preceded by alternating cycles of rest and activity in Golden Ratio. Ocean waves mirror this principle, beginning as imperceptible swells far offshore, slowly building in a series of alternating rising and falling waves, before building into a Golden Spiral as they break and crash ashore. The water then regroups, reversing direction to prepare for the next wave. Even a lightening bolt has retracements—micro rest and recovery cycles—which are vital to the total activity of striking. It's similar to a catapult's loading phase, which we can harness for our health and benefit. Nature reflects this continual back-and-forth wave principle; optimal human movement and performance follows the same golden path.

Dr. Ronald Sandler adapted the Fibonacci Sequence into a peak performance training system. Co-author Matthew Cross (seen here) used it to train for and win a 5k race.

Like the fractal branching patterns of trees, lightning Bolts frequently branch according to Fibonacci Ratios, following Nature's Path of Least Resistance.

Run like Vitruvian Man with Robert Walker's Speed Theorem: Runners like Usain Bolt can maximize speed by tuning strides-per-second to stride length via the Golden Ratio.

Core fitness training is the foundation of total body fitness, integrating our body's upper and lower Golden Ratio segments. All balance exercises build core strength.

Golden Ratio-tuned rest and recovery periods set up a literal catapult effect, allowing you to achieve and maintain new levels of health, fitness and performance.

Kung Fu Master Rob Moses, David Carradine's (*Kill Bill*) trainer, created Golden Spiral-curved PhysioStix, Martial Arts training tools which bring the Universe's power into your hands.

Triathlon legend Dave Scott accessed the power of a Golden Ratio-aligned training schedule en route to 2 of his 6 total Hawaiian Ironman Triathlon victories.

Our muscles will stretch 1.6 times (the Golden Ratio) their resting length before tearing; 1-2 seconds is the maximum recommended time to hold a full stretch.

Golf and biomechanics expert Dr. David Wright found that tuning your stance to Golden Proportions ensures a symmetrical core, essential for an optimal power swing.

Olympian Dawn Saidur combines endurance, strength and flexibility in his 40/30/30 Golden Olympic Training Ratio. The larger (40%) segment favors your chosen sport.

Tennis great Bjorn Borg's pronounced topspin strokes exemplified the graceful power of the Golden Spiral, Nature's Path of Least Resistance/Maximum Performance.

The Golden Ratio Workout Wave, inspired by Dr. Ronald Sandler, tunes workout and recovery periods to Fibonacci Ratios for peak performance and injury reduction.

Fibonacci Interval Training™ (FIT) uses alternating hi-intensity workout/rest periods and exercise reps tuned to Fibonacci numbers, optimizing fitness at minimal time invested.

Tiger Woods and all great golfers' swings naturally mirror the Golden Spiral, which supports maximum power and accuracy with minimum effort. *Holographic Golf* in action.

Champion bodybuilder Casey Viator, a protégé of Nautilus™ inventor Arthur Jones and the youngest Mr. America in history (19), had Golden Ratio body measurements.

Nautilus™ equipment is built on the Golden Spiral and has produced some of history's greatest bodybuilders, from Arnold Schwarzenegger to Casey Viator.

| Relaxed Muscle Length | 1.0 |
| Maximum Muscle Stretch Range | 1.6 |

WB GOLF
WRIGHT BALANCE · BALANCE FOR PERFORMANCE

ENDURANCE = 40%

FLEXIBILITY = 30%

STRENGTH = 30%

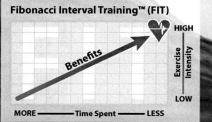

Nautilus

Golden Ratio Workout Wave

5 Waves Up

3 Waves Down

8 Waves Total

The Elliott Wave-inspired Golden Ratio Workout Wave has an up wave and a down wave which are in 5:3 ratio to one another. In the up wave there are 3 waves up and 2 down; in the down wave there are 2 waves down and 1 wave up. These sequenced waves repeat infinitely.

Fibonacci Interval Training™ (FIT)

HIGH

Benefits

Exercise Intensity

LOW

MORE ——— Time Spent ——— LESS

Exercise Reps or Interval Periods (seconds or minutes)

1–1–2–3–5–8–13–21–34–55...

The Divine Proportion is a scale of proportions, which makes the bad difficult and the good easy.

Albert Einstein

Structure

The Great Pyramid is a classic

enigma whose true builders, construction date and purpose remain unknown. We do know that it elegantly exhibits the Golden Ratio/Phi Φ (along with Pi π) with a jeweler's precision. Leading geo-anthropologists such as Graham Hancock (*Fingerprints of the Gods*) propose that it and similar monumental ancient structures were built before the last ice age. If so, this would point to the existence of advanced civilizations on Earth long before currently recorded history that had deep knowledge of the advanced mathematics of the Universe. Such implications are quite compelling.

The Golden Ratio is embedded across the globe in numerous ancient structures and sites, from Mexico's Pyramid of the Sun to Stonehenge, the Parthenon and New Mexico's Chaco Canyon. Classic buildings designed by enlightened architects follow the same universal path. From Europe's great cathedrals, such as Notre Dame, to the Taj Mahal, Beijing's forbidden city's ground plan, New York City's original Penn Station, Grand Central Station, Empire State and United Nations buildings—all are veritable showcases of the Ratio. This explains in part the inspirational magnetism and popularity of these and similar classical structures over time. We are naturally drawn to things that remind us of Nature and the perfected source from which we come. Structures exhibiting aesthetics of the Golden Ratio are naturally pleasing and inspiring, as they carry the Pattern of Life in their sacred designs—the Divine spark igniting and animating all creation.

The Great Pyramid is a timeless treasury of the Golden Ratio. Until the 13th century it was covered with an 8-ft. thick, smooth casing of polished, mirror-like limestone.

San Francisco's Golden Gate Bridge exhibits multiple Golden Ratios in its design, a hidden-in-plain-sight element of its iconic landmark status.

Beijing's Forbidden City, heart of the Chinese Empire and "Middle Kingdom" at the center of the cosmos, is replete with Golden Ratios in its ground plan design.

The Eiffel tower delights the eye and compliments the Parisian skyline with its elegant Golden Ratio symmetry.

India's Taj Mahal, built by Shah Jahan as a memorial to his 3rd wife, is a beautiful expression of Golden Ratio symmetry in architecture on a grand scale.

New York City's Empire State Building showcases several Golden Ratio design elements in its iconic architecture, particularly at its top section.

New York City's beloved Grand Central Terminal, built in 1913, features the Golden Ratio abundantly throughout its classic design.

Multiple Phi Φ proportions are evident in the famous Greek Parthenon, from its Golden Rectangle main façade to progressively smaller aspects of its architecture.

Stonehenge's ground plan features numerous Golden Ratios between the giant stones, reflecting a grand resonance between heaven and earth.

The universality of the Golden Ratio throughout the ancient world is well demonstrated in the great Mexican Pyramid of the Sun.

Medieval architects harnessed the divine inspirational power of the Golden Ratio in their designs, as seen in France's great Chartres Cathedral.

New York's UN building's Golden Rectangular theme was designed by French architect Le Corbusier, who corresponded with Albert Einstein on the Golden Ratio.

New York City's original Penn Station, built in 1910; demolished in 1963, was inspired in part by the Roman Baths of Caracalla, with exquisite Golden Ratio design.

Artistic rendition of the Great Pyramid with its original 8ft-thick polished limestone casing intact.

Good fortune follows the Golden Ratio.
Matthew Cross

Abundance

The Cornucopia is a classic archetype of abundance, borne from its mythical link to Zeus, as a goat's horn endlessly replenished with bountiful riches. This story can be brought to life when we infuse our creative endeavors with the Golden Ratio—golden examples being J.K. Rowling's *Harry Potter* and Dan Brown's *The Da Vinci Code*. Is there an easy and enjoyable way you can bring the magical tale of the Cornucopia to bear in your life? The answer is an abundant *yes*. Even though the Cornucopia is a mythical creation, you can mirror the Golden Ratio and Fibonacci Sequence used in its creation to create your own virtual Cornucopia. Shaped like a Golden Spiral goat's horn, the Cornucopia reflects the Fibonacci Sequence's boundless abundance, a golden stairway of infinite expansion.

You can harness your imagination to the upward spiral of numbers in the sequence… 0, 1, 1, 2, 3, 5, 8, 13, 21… by ascribing each number a corresponding monetary value. This process of virtual financial growth and leverage is outlined in *The Millionaire's MAP*™, an interactive workbook by co-author Matthew Cross. It's a self-led adventure for expanding your imagination to welcome greater prosperity into all areas of your life. The sky is the limit as far as virtual spending goes, so you can truly let go and break the mental bounds of what you would normally allow yourself to imagine and spend. It's like hooking your mind and spirit to the shooting star of compounding interest. Once you get the feel for virtual abundance in the form of Fibonacci dollars spent a quantum door opens, setting into motion unexpected possibilities, prosperity and joy in your physical reality. The process endows you with open sesame access to the abundance and good fortune you desire. You may then call yourself a Cornucopian.

The Cornucopia is a timeless icon of abundance, true to its origins in the infinite Golden Spiral design of creation and growth.

Ben Franklin's eyes are aligned at the Golden Ratio level on the US $100 bill. Many examples of Golden Ratios can be found in currency design worldwide.

Both J.K. Rowling's & Dan Brown's Golden Ratio-tinged books and films are among the most successful in history, with combined sales of over 13 billion dollars.

Credit and debit cards are one of modern society's most popular yet hidden-in-plain-sight archetypes of the Golden Ratio, as both are Golden Rectangles.

The infinite Fibonacci Sequence is a great Golden Key and principle that can be harnessed to imagine and manifest greater abundance in all areas of your life.

Da Vinci's Vitruvian Man appears on Italy's One Euro coin, imprinting the idealized Golden Ratio man on over 1.6 billion coins in circulation throughout Europe.

Ancient Egyptian coin featuring a Cornucopia horn of plenty and good fortune, whose Golden Spiral shape reflects the infinitely expanding Fibonacci Sequence.

The Fibonacci-based Elliott Wave is at the core of Robert Prechter, Jr.'s stock forecasting system. Prechter also created the Golden Ratio field of Socionomics.

All eggs–not just the Golden Goose's–are Golden Eggs, having Golden Proportions of length to width. This universal archetype is a key to wisdom, abundance and success.

The Millionaire's Map stair-steps you to greater abundance via an ingenious method, like compounding interest, to ignite the Fibonacci Sequence's power in your life.

1.618

AMERICAN EXPRESS
CORPORATE
0112 358 13 2134
05/08   1235
L. FIBONACCI

011235...

$$$

Elliott Wave

```
              5
         3        7
      1   4    6     8
        2
```

1 2
3
5
4
6
7
8

5 Waves Up   3 Waves Down

8 Waves Total

TOTAL AMOUNT SPENT OVER 21 DAYS

SPENDING AMOUNT	100	100	200	300	500	800	1,300	2,100	3,400	5,500	8,900	14,400	23,300	37,700	61,000	98,700	159,700	258,400	418,100	676,500	1,094,600	2,865,600
DAY	1	2	3	4	5	6	7	8	9	10	11	12	13	14	15	16	17	18	19	20	21	

89

The great Golden Spiral seems to be Nature's way of building quantity without sacrificing quality.

William Hoffer

Business Success

Key Golden Ratio hallmarks are growth, harmony and success in every measure. This includes efficiency, doing more with less, working smarter vs. harder and enjoying growing results, in work and in life. The Golden Ratio principle applied lights the way to more effortless leverage and success, reflected in companies such as Apple, Toyota, Starbucks, Siemens, Twitter and Anastasia Beverly Hills. Whenever the Ratio is applied in life or business, both begin a robust journey of continuous improvement, a principle illustrated in quality genius Dr. W. Edwards Deming's *Kaizen* (Continuous Improvement) Helix.

Dr. Deming taught that work transformation begins with personal transformation. By optimizing our life and work systems and better balancing work/personal time, greater joy and productivity in work and life results. It's like positioning a fulcrum under a lever—when properly placed, lifting or achieving anything is more effortless. Archimedes could easily have been referring to a Golden Ratio placement of his famous lever when he said, *Give me a place to stand and a lever long enough and I will move the world*. Utilizing the Ratio to tune any business aspect—from working time ratios, decision making, financial and compensation percentages, design of plant, products, services, logos, marketing— leverages Nature's Golden Growth Spiral, lifting any business to ever-greater heights. When the synergy, value and delight arising from parts coming together in a greater whole are sustained, greater loyalty and success is inevitable. The Golden Ratio is a *Foundational* life and business organizing principle, inspiring right *Actions*, leading to better and bigger *Results*.

The Golden Google Ratio can be seen in the proportions of the letters in the logo of the world's #1 search engine. Many leading logos have similar clear Golden Proportions.

#1 automobile brand Toyota is a model of the Golden Ratio attributes of quality, efficiency and profitability. Toyota's logo (like Apple's) is also in elegant Golden Proportion.

The eyes have it: the Golden Ratio is brewed into Starbucks' logo and in coffee beans' Golden Proportions—hidden success factors behind caffé culture worldwide.

Twitter's web page and logo are designed with Golden Ratios, which greatly enhance efficiency of communication and data impact in human information processing.

Apple's iconic logo reflects the Golden Ratio as do many Apple products and OS icons. Our graphic analysis overlay reveals 1.6:1 ratios between the Apple's contours, byte and leaf.

Apple's iCloud logo features two sets of circles in 1.6:1 ratio. In a nested Golden Ratio harmonic, the beautifully rounded cloud fits neatly inside a Golden Rectangle.

Apple adopted a **G**olden **R**atio-**I**mprinted **D**esign **GRID** for all iOS 7 icons, resulting in a more harmonious, unified theme which enhances navigation and is easier on the eyes.

As with all icons in Apple's iOS 7, the new Photos icon elegantly reflects its Golden Ratio design GRID origins, enhancing the human+software interface.

Quality genius Dr. W. Edward Deming's Plan-Do-Study-Act *Kaizen* (Jap., *Continuous Improvement*) helix, the great Golden Spiral-like success cycle supporting top businesses.

Hotel Indigo is the world's first hotel chain designed with the Golden Ratio throughout structure and theme, creating a warm, welcoming environment for guests.

Management guru Frederick Reichheld's loyalty/disloyalty scale shifts near the Golden Ratio. Loyal client growth is the #1 predictor of profit growth in all business.

The Now & Zen Co. operates on Golden Ratio principles, producing beautiful lifestyle products, e.g., the Zen Alarm Clock, which awakens you with Fibonacci-spaced tones.

Anastasia Soare's Golden Ratio eyebrow sculpting system is the foundation of her worldwide natural beauty empire, whose clients include Oprah, JLo and Madonna.

The double-entry accounting system, foundation of world commerce, was pioneered in 1494 by Fra Luca Pacioli, author of *The Divine Proportion* and a key mentor of Da Vinci.

The Hoshin Kanri (*Jap., Compass, Way*) strategic alignment system supports dynamic leverage and growth, via its 40/30/30 Foundation-Actions-Results™ (FAR) Golden Ratio priority sequence.

Archimedes said: *Give me a place to stand and a lever long enough and I will move the world.* The Golden Ratio is a veritable golden lever for achievement excellence.

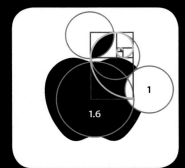

Deming
PDSA Quality Cycle

HOTEL
indigo™

Φ

1 2 3 4 5 6 | 7 8 9 10

◄— More Disloyal/Loss | More Loyal/Profit —►

Loyalty Scale

Now & Zen

ANASTASIA
Beverly Hills ™

Results 30%

Actions 30%

Foundation 40%

方針
Hoshin Kanri

Φ

A theory [e.g., the Golden Ratio] is more impressive the greater is the simplicity of its premise, the more different are the kinds of things it relates and the more extended its range of applicability.

Albert Einstein

Learning & Genius Activation

Everybody is a genius, Albert Einstein once said. We all have genius potential in our own, wonderfully unique way. All it takes to ignite the spark within is exposure to a universal activation agent. The Golden Ratio and Fibonacci Sequence are such ignition and booster catalysts, abundantly present within and without everywhere we look. This is true in Nature especially, as Leonardo Da Vinci sagely observed: *The wisest and noblest teacher is Nature herself.*

Recognizing Nature's patterns woven throughout existence awakens our natural pattern recognition skills. The simple act of pattern recognition—the ability to freely connect the dots across disciplines to discover and divine greater meaning— is a master learning and genius activation agent at any age. Learning to recognize Golden Ratio patterns is a great, fun way to increase your brain's associative connections. An increased number of association fibers raised Einstein's thinking to genius level. As Albert Szent-Gyorgyi (Vitamin C discoverer) said, *Discovery consists of seeing what everybody has seen and thinking what nobody has thought.* This is exactly what Golden Ratio pattern recognition offers. It's an open secret for inspiration and learning available to anyone, anytime, e.g., Apple co-founder Steve Wozniak was inspired in college to create a Fibonacci-based infinite-loop program and later utilized Fibonacci coding in his legendary work at Apple. Integrating the Golden Ratio into your life, learning and work at any level is a golden key to activating your unique genius, staying agile and sharp, discovering the riches within and making a difference in your life and in the world.

As a boy Albert Einstein activated his latent genius powers of pattern recognition looking for Fibonacci Sequence numbers and patterns throughout Nature.

Donald in Mathmagic Land, one of Walt Disney's most popular educational films (Academy Award nominee, 1959), features a delightful Golden Ratio learning adventure.

One of young Albert Einstein's passions in pursuit of greater knowledge of the Universe was counting petals on daisies in search of the Fibonacci Sequence.

Shells, pinecones and starfish are among Nature's most prominent Golden Ratio icons, which can be displayed both for their beauty and genius activation power.

The Mandelbrot Set fractal reveals its self-similar unity of form across an infinite scale of size. Golden Ratios abound in this master fractal, a Golden Key to chaos theory.

The Golden Rectangle, Triangle and Spiral used in picture taking/cropping enhances any subject's beauty and magnetism. Photos by Wayne Radford.

Looking for and appreciating the countless Golden Ratio and Fibonacci Sequence appearances in the world around us lights up our creativity and unique, innate genius.

Cat (and dog) claws are playful hidden-in-plain sight Golden Spirals, a fun way to engage children in the hunt for the Pattern of Life all around us.

Golden Ratio calipers are an easy and fun way to reveal and work with the Golden Ratio in any creative endeavor.

Ambidexterity is one of Golden Ratio master Leonardo Da Vinci's easy genius activation exercises that we can utilize. Try it when eating, brushing teeth, writing, sports, etc.

Light switch plates are perfect Golden Rectangles in plain sight, reminding us of the Golden Ratio's power to light up our unique genius. Turn it on!

Fibonacci coding is a self-synchronizing method for encoding positive Fibonacci number-based integers into binary code words, optimizing coding efficiency.

Mathematician Edouard Zeckendorf's Theorem proves that any integer can be represented with Fibonacci number sums, a key component of Fibonacci coding.

A MindMap of the Golden Ratio's key facets: Golden Ratio Line, Rectangle, Spiral, Star, Triangle and Fibonacci Sequence. MindMaps enhance creativity, learning and memory.

Stars and spirals are classic shapes in the Golden Ratio family. It's no surprise that they are among the favorite shapes in both children's drawings and ancient motifs.

233

There is a geometry of art as there is a geometry of life, and as the Greeks had guessed, they happen to be the same.

Matila Ghyka

Culture & the Arts

The Universal prevalence of the Golden Ratio as a central design code of great and enduring art is as indisputable as it is ubiquitous throughout culture and creation. From ancient Egyptian masterworks to Greek vases, Da Vinci's *Mona Lisa*, Botticelli's *Venus*, Dali's *Sacrament of the Last Supper*, to Jamie Wyeth's classic portrait of John F. Kennedy, we find Nature's premier design code at work and play. It provides a timeless "moment of truth," which is how Tom Hanks (as Robert Langdon) describes utilizing the Fibonacci Sequence as the password to access a vital clue and treasure in *The Da Vinci Code* film. These are all catalysts for cultural evolution and enlightenment.

The infinite manifestations of great art, whether visual, musical or poetic, always delight our senses and inspire to the degree that they elevate our spirit towards higher states. Golden Ratio art does this because it embodies the principle of aspiration towards perfection. Such art cultivates a sense of oneness in the viewer—art and man becoming one for a time—reflecting the infinite dance towards unity at play throughout the Universe. One of the key descriptors for culture is *pattern*; when higher order patterns such as the Golden Ratio are prevalent in any culture, greater harmony, refinement and unity are natural results. Beauty, truth and goodness are among its prime constants. The Ratio is like a universal cultural North Star, in that it reminds us of and leads us towards the perfected source from which we come. The sublime, elegant pattern of life which infuses great art is a touchstone for great culture and thus the higher ideals and ideas of mankind.

Jamie Wyeth's *Portrait of JFK* (1967), a classic painting in oil which showcases the power of the Golden Ratio to focus the viewer's attention on the iconic image.

Numerous Beatles' songs, like many popular songs, feature clear Golden Ratio demarcations: a change in tempo or theme occurs at the song's .38 and/or .62 point.

Walt Disney drew a Golden Star as his template to create Mickey Mouse's iconic face; Donald Duck learned of the Golden Ratio in *Donald in MathMagic Land* (1959).

Leonardo Da Vinci's *Mona Lisa* (c. 1503-06) as well as many great works of art across time are constructed with Golden Ratio elements, resulting in their timeless appeal.

The elusive *Golden Snitch* in J.K. Rowling's *Harry Potter* game of Quidditch rhymes with *Goldene Schnitt*—which means *Golden Ratio* in German. Wizardly coincidence?

The climax of history's #1 music video, Michael Jackson's *Thriller* (1983), is at its .62 Golden Ratio point, as Jackson transforms into a mesmerizing dancing zombie.

Superman's iconic "S" emblem is a diamond pentagon in Golden Ratio. Is the legendary Man of Steel also the Man of Ratio?

Darren Aronofsky's 1998 film *Pi* is a psychological thriller involving number theory. The film also features Phi Φ—the Golden Ratio and Fibonacci Sequence.

Many musical instruments including the violin owe their beautiful resonance to their Golden Ratio design, while piano keys' layout follows the Fibonacci Sequence.

Many composers' classic works feature the Golden Ratio and Fibonacci Sequence, including those of Mozart (pictured here), Debussy, Bartok and Bach.

Artist Mario Merz used the Fibonacci Sequence in his Arte Povera work to represent the universal principles of procreation, growth and harmony (at Rome's Forum).

Dan Brown's *The Da Vinci Code* book and film featuring Tom Hanks and Audrey Tautou brilliantly re-introduced the Golden Ratio/Phi Φ and the Fibonacci Sequence to the world.

The medium enhances the message: Golden Ratio typography and design maximize quality and efficiency of content cognition, as advocated by design pioneers like Chris Pearson.

Playing cards are also hidden-in-plain-sight Golden Ratio cards: as with all credit cards, their dimensions form a Golden Rectangle.

National Geographic's Golden Rectangle logo subtly illustrates the concept that all of the world can be viewed through the infinite window of the Golden Ratio.

In design, form and function many of Apple's products embody the Golden Ratio (e.g., Apple's iOS 7 icons), a key factor in their user delight, loyalty and worldwide success.

Tim Kring's *Touch* with Kiefer Sutherland, & Nicolas Falacci/Cheryl Heuton's *NUMB3RS* with Rob Morrow & David Krumholtz feature the Golden Ratio & Fibonacci Sequence.

16:10 aspect ratio widescreen monitors reflect the optimal human visual perception field, which neatly fits the proportional boundaries of a horizontal Golden Rectangle.

iTunes

Let It Be

2:24 ◆ −1:30

62%   Φ   38%

Harry Potter

THE DA VINCI CODE

DAN BROWN

THE DA VINCI CODE

π

Line Height 1.618   Font Size 1.0   Key

K ♠

1.618

1.0

TOUCH

NUMB3RS
THE COMPLETE FIRST SEASON

377

Every part is disposed to unite with the whole, that it may thereby escape from its own incompleteness.

Leonardo Da Vinci

Spirit

The quest for the Divine is perhaps humanity's greatest. At its root is a quest for an affirmation of meaning, connection and communion with a greater whole. Unity is at the very heart of this quest. Even though we may appear separate, we innately sense our similarity to and resonance with this greater whole, our divine fractal reflection. The Golden Ratio is the master formula for unity: the division of a line where the larger part of the line to the smaller part is the same as the ratio of the whole line to the larger part. A greater whole is always the natural result. We become increasingly aware of this Divine pattern all around us as we increase our learning of it, which further enhances our perception of unity within and without. And our ability to perceive unity enhances our ability to create and share greater value, as integral theorist Stephen McIntosh has noted.

Activating the Divine in one's life can be as simple as recognizing the Golden Ratio patterns found everywhere, and then using this revelation to honor the sacred interconnectedness of all. It's beyond coincidence that a prime thread, although sometimes hidden, woven throughout the philosophy and symbology of the world's many spiritual paths is the unity pattern of the Golden Ratio, unsurprisingly also known as the *Divine* Proportion. The Universe is clearly animated by *Something Great*, notes renowned DNA researcher Dr. Kazuo Murakami; paradoxically, the Universe also offers infinite manifestations of the One. The Golden Ratio is a golden key for the harmonious unification of any parts into a greater whole, which exceeds the sum of those parts. Contemplating this simple truth opens wide the door of consciousness, individually and collectively, to the Divine.

The 5 Elements of traditional Chinese philosophy are a blueprint of Universal energy movement, superimposed on the Golden Ratio-based pentagram.

Yoga is an ancient science of health, enlightenment and union. The heart chakra is at the Golden Ratio bridge point and unifies upper and lower chakras.

The Flower of Life, found in ancient ruins worldwide. Keys to sacred knowledge, e.g., the Tree of Life and Platonic solids, lie within its Golden Ratio-rich geopatterns.

Jewish Kabbalists use the Golden Ratio-blueprinted Tree of Life to depict a cosmological model of creation and spiritual evolution.

The ancient Egyptian Ankh or Key of Life is a sacred Golden Proportioned amulet featured in their hieroglyphs and carried by the Egyptian Gods.

The Chartres Labyrinth in France has Golden Ratio design elements (see pg. 52). Labyrinths resemble the human brain and are ancient, sacred pathways to the Divine.

The Golden Ratio is embedded in plain sight in the design of the ancient Cross; viewed on its side it reflects the classic Golden Ratio 1.618 to 1 line diagram.

Visionary William Blake's *Ancient of Days* shows God creating the Universe in Divine Proportion with golden calipers. Blake was a favorite of Apple co-founder Steve Jobs.

AUM (or OM) is the ancient Indian symbol for the primordial sound of the Universe. The letters A, U, M correspond to alphabet numbers 1, 21 and 13: Fibonacci numbers.

The Star of David, symbol of Judaism also known in ancient times as the Seal of Solomon, is also infused with Golden Ratio geometry.

Statues of the Buddha invariably display Golden Ratio symmetry. Buddhism's central tenants emphasize the unification of all life in a divine spirit of compassion and grace.

The classic Golden Ratio line drawing illustrates the essential integrative, unity function, where two parts come together to form a greater whole: 1 + 1 = 3.

In Eastern philosophy the Tao signifies the Universe's primordial essence/fundamental Nature, while the homonym Tau τ is a classic term for the Golden Ratio. Divine coincidence?

Classic cathedrals like Notre Dame are designed with the Golden Ratio, bringing Nature's Divinely Proportioned glory into structures for divine communion.

Sacred Islamic tiling designs (Shah Mosque, Isfahan, Iran, c. 1453) exhibit beautiful Golden Ratio geometry and infinite patterns, similar to modern Penrose tilings.

According to the Bible, the design of both the fabled Ark of the Covenant and Noah's Ark contain near-perfect Golden Rectangles.

Andrew Rogers' 50-ton sculpture *Ratio* in Jerusalem is dedicated to unity and peace, a numerical palindrome in a rising/falling Fibonacci Sequence: 1,1,2,3,5,8,5,3,2,1,1.

Wood 木 (Mù)

Water 水 (Shuǐ)

Fire 火 (Huǒ)

Metal 金 (Jīn)

Earth 土 (Tǔ)

1.618   1.0

62%   38%

Φ

A   B

A + B

A + B is to A as A is to B

Perhaps there is a pattern set up in the heavens for one who desires to see it, and having seen it, to find it in himself.

Plato

The Golden Renaissance Code

The Golden Ratio and Fibonacci

Sequence light an infinite path forward towards a newer, more harmonious world. Their sacred imprints are touchstones for the universal connections that unite all creation. We know we're on the right path as we begin to recognize patterns of the Divine Proportion in our lives. A renaissance of wonder, hope and commitment arises when we realize that we're all connected through a unity principle pointing to a grand totality exceeding the sum of its parts. At the heart of this renaissance is learning and imagination— a passion to think different, dream bigger and integrate universal principles such as the Golden Ratio into our lives. Accessing this timeless touchstone of unification fires the imagination and allows us to rise above a misplaced belief that separation rules reality.

The Golden Ratio has infused renaissances throughout history. Looking back, we can call forth inspiration from geniuses such as Pythagoras, Da Vinci and Einstein, who used the Golden Ratio and Fibonacci Sequence as evolutionary touchstones in their epochs. As a bridge to the newer worlds we wish to create, we need only engage this Divine pattern with wisdom and grace and learn to cultivate it within and without, knowing that whatever we value and appreciate grows.

John Lennon shared words that reflect the Divine Proportion's underlying message of unity and harmony when he sang, *Imagine all the people, living life in peace… You may say I'm a dreamer, but I'm not the only one. I hope someday you'll join us, and the world will be as one…*

Imagine, the John Lennon memorial at Strawberry Fields in New York's Central Park, with superimposed Golden Spiral galaxy. The rise of the Golden Ratio in popular culture heralds a renaissance of unity, peace, love and imagination, inviting us to engage anew Albert Einstein's timeless wisdom:

Imagination is more important than knowledge. For knowledge is limited to all we now know and understand, while imagination embraces the entire world, and all there ever will be to know and understand… Logic will take you from A to B. Imagination will take you everywhere…

Awareness of the Golden Section can reveal the seams of things and the nodes of being that almost all of us miss in this contingent phase of existence.

Guy Murchie

Puzzlers &
Genius Activators

At the heart of all puzzles and

great questions is an adventure to solve problems, find greater meaning and transform uncertainty and incoherence into coherent knowing and a sense of unity. Exercises that stretch the mind to connect the dots and engage in pattern recognition are a sure path to activating one's genius potential and keeping the mind young. These skills transfer to our larger lives. Engaging any new challenge calls forth our latent creative talents and gifts. Playing with the Golden Ratio and Fibonacci Sequence offers countless opportunities in this regard by contemplating their ubiquitous appearance at every opportunity. This is enough to unleash a quest of exploration and discovery that lifts the entirety and scope of one's perspective. Realizing that application of the Golden Ratio and Fibonacci Sequence reveals the way to peak learning, performance and achievement gives one profound wisdom to navigate life. Perhaps ultimately, puzzles are about discovering the answers to our greatest questions: *Who are we? Why are we here? Where did we come from? Where are we going?* Such questions hint at their answers.

The enjoyable exercises that follow enhance your ability to shift perspectives, expand your perception and increase your range of capabilities. Anytime you consciously look for patterns, which are often hidden in events, data, pictures or behavior, you activate your innate Golden Ratio intelligence. Practicing Pattern Recognition amplifies your natural ability to "Connect the D●t's" and see the unified big picture, which allows us to perceive, receive and add more value. Expanded perception is nothing less than genius activation, helping us to contemplate the greatest puzzle of all—the mystery of life.

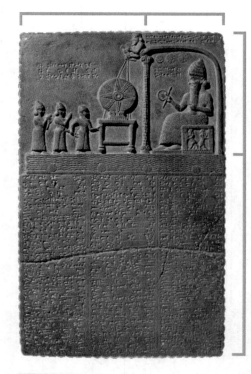

The Golden Rectangle Tablet of Shamash is a 3,000 year-old tablet from Mesopotamia/Sumer (present-day Iraq). It preserves and transmits multiple elements of knowledge across time: clearly visible language inscriptions, pictures and clear yet hidden-in-plain sight Golden Ratio wisdom. Here is a classic case of *content* (words and pictures) and *context* (the tablet's Golden Ratio design, through which the data on it is presented). This tablet with multiple levels of Golden Ratio information is an ancient echo to media visionary Marshall McLuhan, who famously said that *The Medium is the Message*.

Modern "tablets" such as Twitter have adopted the same ancient (in reality, timeless) Golden Ratio design medium for their communication templates. Twitter's web page and logo are designed with Golden Ratios, which enhance efficiency of communication and data impact in human information processing.

Research with fMRI scans has shown that at a primal, preconscious level we are hard-wired to recognize and gravitate to the beauty of Golden Ratio proportions. Couple this with research showing that initial impressions of websites can occur in as little as 50-milliseconds and we now have a potent means to increase receptivity of information by embedding the Golden Ratio in the medium used to transmit the message. These and other fascinating research insights into more effective messaging and neural-networking can be found in Roger Dooley's book, *Brainfluence*.

Divine Order Out of Chaos with the Stereogram

Stereograms are specially generated double images: the first is an obvious image of seemingly random, chaotic and disconnected images or dots. The second is a "hidden" 3D image, which can only be seen when you gaze at the image in a special, relaxed way. In addition to being an excellent tool for expanding your visual perception and pattern recognition skills, stereograms are also often used by vision therapists in the treatment of many binocular vision and accommodative disorders.

Try it: Focus your gaze on a point about 2/3rds of the way between you and the picture, letting your eyes de-focus and cross slightly, almost as if you're daydreaming. You might try holding a finger up at about the 2/3 point between you and the picture and focus your gaze on your finger. After anywhere from 10 seconds to a minute or so, the 3-D "hidden" image should slowly appear and come into focus. If it takes a little longer, that's ok. No rush. Hint—the shape is one of the 5 primary patterns of the Golden Ratio.

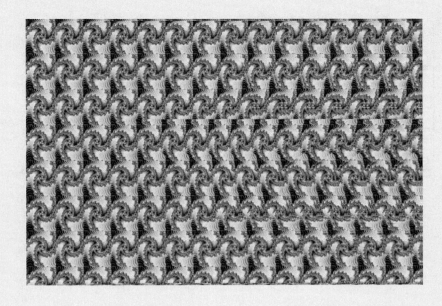

The "Greater Whole" 3-D Dodecahedron

A dodecahedron's pentagonal Golden Ratio structure is one of the Platonic solids and is a primary building block of the Universe. Look at these two side-by-side images of dodecahedrons, with a relaxed gaze. Focus your gaze on a point about 2/3rds of the way between you and the picture, letting your eyes de-focus and cross slightly, almost as if you're daydreaming. After anywhere from 10 seconds to a minute or so, it will seem as if the two separate images slowly come together and merge into a 3D dodecahedron. This is a fun and simple example of two parts coming together to form a greater (in this case, 3-D), whole.

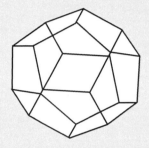

The Rabbit Riddle: Origin of the Fibonacci Sequence

An intriguing mathematical puzzle posed in the third section of Leonardo Fibonacci's book from 1228 A.D., *Liber Abaci*, introduced the world to Nature's prime method of growth and manifesting abundance. In his book, Leonardo poses this seemingly simple question:

How many pairs of rabbits can be produced from a single pair in one year if it is assumed that every month each pair begets a new pair, which from the second month becomes productive? (translation from *Encyclopedia Britannica*)

To restate the quiz: Begin with a single pair of rabbits. Every month, each productive pair bears a new pair, which then becomes productive when they are one month old. How many pairs of rabbits will there be after twelve months? See if you can figure it out first from studying the rabbit graph at right. Hint: there's a pattern in the number of increasing pairs...

Answer: 144 pairs total. Month by month, the number of new rabbit pairs reveals and follows the Fibonacci Sequence: after 1 month, there is **1** pair; 2 months, **1** pair; 3 months, **2** pairs; 4 months, **3** pairs; 5 months, **5** pairs; 6 months, **8** pairs; 7 months, **13** pairs; 8 months, **21** pairs; 9 months, **34** pairs; 10 months, **55** pairs; 11 months, **89** pairs; 12 months, **144** pairs. As botanists and biologists discovered centuries later, Fibonacci's magically mysterious Sequence manifests everywhere throughout Nature. *Note: The rabbit illustration repeated at right is entitled "Young Hare" and was painted by Golden Ratio master artist Albrecht Druer in 1504.*

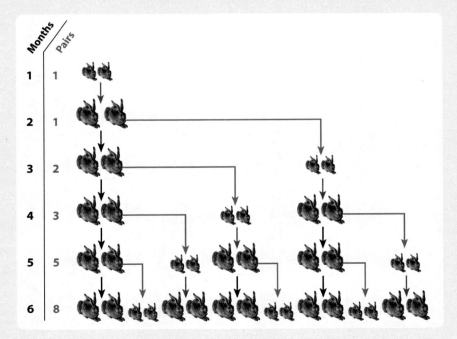

Q. **What are the Golden Ratio Secrets hidden-in-plain sight with Audrey Tautou and her character Sophie in *The Da Vinci Code* film?**

Answers ahead on next pages.

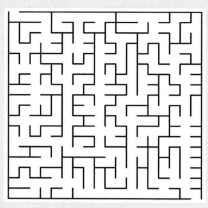

Classic Maze

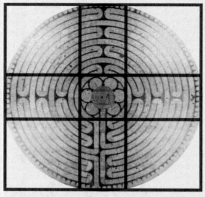

The walking Labyrinth at France's Chartres Cathedral (c. 1220) is 42 feet/13 meters in diameter. Shown with overlaid Golden Ratio grid.

Maze of Chaos vs. Labyrinth to a Higher Order

Q: What is the difference between a Maze and a Labyrinth? Study the two examples of each shown here. Any differences that stand out to you? A key distinction: A Maze has many false starts, dead ends and no clear sense of direction, with the associated uncertainty and stress those attributes can encourage. A Labyrinth, on the other hand, has no false starts or dead ends. Instead, it offers a clear direction to the goal of its center, always evolving forward along an assured, focused yet playful path.

France's Chartres Labyrinth, pictured here, is perhaps the world's most famous. Designed on the sacred matrix of the Golden Ratio and uncannily resembling the human brain's contours, Labyrinths are ancient, sacred paths for communion with the Divine. Even viewing one can be a form of meditation, as can tracing its path with your finger or eyes (use the large labyrinth on page 47 to experiment with tracing exercises). Walking the Labyrinth can be a sacred journey for those on a conscious path of inner awareness and enlightenment.

Golden Ratio Word Search Puzzler

As with crossword puzzles, word search puzzles are excellent for developing pattern recognition and new association skills in the brain. This serves to improve memory and abstract thinking skills. This word search puzzle is also a 13 x 21 Fibonacci/Golden Rectangle matrix and has over 40 hidden words related to the Golden Ratio. See how many you can circle. Buona Fortuna!

I	E	L	P	R	O	P	O	R	T	I	O	N
R	D	Y	N	O	M	R	A	H	H	A	N	D
A	O	V	D	N	A	S	P	I	R	A	L	G
C	C	6	1	8	T	Y	H	F	E	E	E	O
A	E	I	N	S	T	E	I	N	L	L	D	L
T	N	A	C	I	S	U	M	A	P	G	O	D
H	I	M	N	S	S	E	Q	U	E	N	C	E
E	V	U	D	G	T	E	O	T	K	A	S	N
D	I	C	N	I	V	A	D	I	6	T	D	R
R	D	R	B	A	M	C	R	L	2	C	O	A
A	X	O	W	Y	K	A	D	U	3	E	G	T
L	B	W	O	M	A	N	R	S	8	R	A	I
A	Y	T	U	A	E	B	W	Y	F	W	I	O
R	S	Y	S	O	M	A	N	I	P	A	A	N
Y	H	T	H	R	E	E	B	Y	F	I	V	E
T	R	X	E	F	L	O	O	Y	O	U	O	2
I	I	I	L	U	N	A	D	X	K	T	K	8
N	M	S	L	A	O	P	Y	A	A	L	A	3
I	P	I	C	S	U	N	F	L	O	W	E	R
R	A	C	I	G	A	M	P	A	N	M	P	A
T	I	G	E	N	I	U	S	G	A	L	F	M

Find the Golden Ratio in Your Own Fibonacci Birthday Sequence

Leonardo Fibonacci's "Rabbit Riddle" first delineated the infinite and mysterious Sequence that bears his name: where each successive number is always the sum of the previous two: 0, 1, 1, 2, 3, 5, 8, 13, 21... The Sequence rapidly gives rise to the Golden Ratio: 1.618... that elusive, infinite number approached ever more closely by the ratio of any two successive numbers in the Sequence. However, the Golden Ratio is not specific to Fibonacci's Sequence. *Any two numbers* added together generates a third number, which when added to the previous number gives rise to another, and so on. When repeated 6 to 10 times, this additive process will *always* generate successive numbers that amazingly produce ever-finer Golden Ratio approximations—a magical mathematical mystery!

Try it: Take your birth month and date for example and add them together to get a third number. For example, June 18th would be: **6 + 18 = 24**

Then, combine the new **third** number with the one before it to produce a fourth number: **18 + 24 = 42**

Repeat this process and you'll find that after 6 to 10 times, the ratio between the numbers in your unique sequence *always* converge to 1.618... the Golden Ratio:

6 + 18 = **24**   18 + 24 = **42**   24 + 42 = **66**   42 + 66 = **108**
66 + 108 = **174**   108 + 174 = **282**   174 + 282 = **456**   282 + 456 = **738**

Then, divide the last two sequential numbers: 738 ÷ 456 = **1.618...**

The actual Sequence in this example is: 6, 18, 24, 42, 66, 108, 174, 282, 456, 738...

In this case, the Golden Ratio 1.618 showed up at the 10th iteration. You can check the ratios at each stage to see how close you're getting to 1.618. If you happen to have a Fibonacci Sequence birthday (1/1, 1/2, 2/3, 3/5, 5/8 or 8/13) then you know where this is going fast! Fibonacci's genius described the base fractal of this process starting with just 0, 1, 1... Yet you can always create your own customized Sequence revealing the Golden Ratio using any two numbers that have meaning for you. The popular method detailed above, using the first two numbers of your birthday, is described by Bulent Atalay in his excellent book, *Math and the Mona Lisa: The Art and Science of Leonardo da Vinci.*

The Icnerdblie Pweor of Paettrn Rcgoeinoitn

Aoccdrnig to rscheearch at Cmabrigde Uinervtsiy, it deosn't mttaer in waht oredr the ltteers in a wrod are, the olny iprmoetnt tihng is taht the frist and lsat ltteer be in the rghit pclae. Tihs is bcecuase our biarn is ptrety amzanig at rcgoeinznig paettnrs and fnidnig odrer in smeenig chaos. By smilpy raednig this pragarpah, you are atciavtnig yuor pweors of paettrn rcgoeinoitn, a key hllamrak of Gloedn Rtiao gneuis. Cnorgtluaionts!

What does "Fib" refer to?

a. Leonardo Fibonacci's nickname
b. Fibonacci In Betting
c. Fibonacci Sequence-based poetry
d. A white lie
e. Slang for a heart defibrillator

Circle your selection; Answers ahead on next pages.

How can you represent the 6 key facets of the Golden Ratio in one graphic?

Answers ahead on next pages.

When asked if they were a fan of the Fibonacci Sequence, which superstar musician replied:

How can you not be? It's everywhere; it's all around…

a. John Lennon
b. Tina Turner
c. Bono
d. Madonna
e. Bruce Springsteen

Circle your selection.

Girl With a Watering Can
Renoir's classic painting is the 2nd most popular painting at the National Gallery of Art in Washington, D.C. Can you spot where the painting's three most prominent Golden Ratios align? See next page for answer.

Note: Salvador Dali's *The Sacrament of the Last Supper* is the Gallery's most popular painting. Could this be due to Dali being a Golden Ratio master who embedded it multiple times in his stunning work of surrealism?

What day of the year does Phi Day fall on?

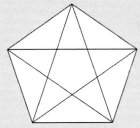

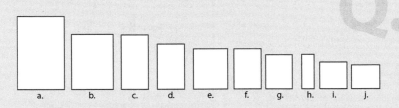

How Many Golden Triangles Can You Find?
Within the pentagon/pentagram are many different kinds of Golden Triangles, with at least 30 Golden Triangles in total. How many different Golden Triangles can you find?

Dr. Fechner's Golden Rectangle Experiment
Golden Proportions can be accurately recognized amidst non-Golden Proportions, as proven by psychologist Gustav Fechner. In a Fechner study in the late 1800's, a group of subjects were asked to rate a series of rectangles according to which they found most pleasing. The winning rectangles displayed Golden Ratio proportions. In-the-know product designers and advertisers have since capitalized on this profound yet simple fact; the Golden Ratio is present in the ratios of everything from ads to credit cards to computer hardware and software to furniture. The typical buyer will instinctively tend to purchase products best clothed in Golden Ratio design. Economics, psychology and sacred geometry have intersected with Fechner's experiment. See how attuned your eye is to the Golden Ratio by circling the Golden Rectangle(s) from among the examples above.

Phyllotaxis describes plant's optimal, Fibonacci Sequence-resonant growth pattern. What does Phylotaxis (one "L") describe?

How is Kiefer Sutherland's character Martin Bohm in the Fox television series *Touch* related to the Golden Ratio?

What lightning-fast Olympian perfectly exemplifies the Golden Sleep Ratio by getting at least 9 hours of sleep every night by saying:

Sleep is extremely important to me—I need to rest and recover in order for the training I do to be absorbed by my body?

Fun Questions regarding Fibonacci Numbers
Why is 0 also known as the Golden Seed or egg, the promising void at the beginning of all things? • When does 1+1=3? • Why are 5 Stars used to signify highest quality? • Why does every human's outline with limbs outstretched form a 5-pointed star? • Why is 13 also known as a lucky number, e.g., a "Bakers Dozen"? • Why is the brain's initial new habit engravement cycle 21 days long? • How do the numbers 21 and 34 contain all of the first 10 numbers? • The first time the Golden Ratio makes its appearance accurate to four digits (1.618) in the Fibonacci Sequence is between the numbers 55 and 89. Why? • Why does it take 233 stacked U.S. dollar bills to equal exactly one inch? For answers visit: www.GoldenRatioBook.com

How is the hat of most every wizard, witch, sorcerer and party reveler related to the Golden Ratio?

Leonardo Fibonacci, The Genius of Pisa Quiz
In addition to his famous namesake Sequence 0,1,1,2,3,5,8,13,21…, which reveals the Golden Ratio 1.618… in the ratio between adjacent numbers in the Sequence, Leonardo Fibonacci (c. 1170 – c. 1250) is also responsible for the introduction to the western world of 3 monumental contributions to mankind, which are literally the foundation for the world we live in today. What are they? Hint: they are present in this paragraph. For the surprising answers, visit http://www.GoldenRatioBook.com

Answers ahead on next pages.

Golden Ratio Magic Squares

[Magic Squares] were highly regarded by the mathematicians of antiquity, who took them as paradigms for natural laws.

John Michell, Golden Ratio genius.

Magic Squares' astounding ability to integrate numbers with a sense of unity is similar to the Golden Ratio's ability to unify separate parts into a greater whole. In the first example shown here, we see the sequential numbers 618, signifying the Golden Ratio. All vertical, horizontal and diagonal rows add up to 15. The second is excerpted from Golden Ratio master Albrecht Druer's famed engraving *Melencholia*. It is designed such that all numbers in all directions add up to the Fibonacci Number 34. Amazingly, there are more embedded combinations of numbers that add up to 34 (a Fibonacci number) beyond the vertical, horizontal and diagonal, such as the sum of the 4 outer squares and also the sum of the 4 inner squares. To top it all off, Drurer somehow managed to also incorporate the year he created the square (1514) in the numbers along the square's bottom row.

2	7	6
9	5	1
4	3	8

Pay Attention to the Golden Ratio Signs *Everywhere*

From now on, you may start noticing the appearance of key numbers of the Golden Ratio and Fibonacci Sequence in your daily life:

618 62 382 38 1618

0 1 1 2 3 5 8 13 21 34 55 89 144 233 377 610 987 1597...

As you learn about and contemplate their ubiquitousness in the Universe, you may become aware of them showing up in Receipts, Ticket Numbers, Travel Times, News Statistics, Road Signs, Street Numbers, Phone Numbers, etc., etc. This can be a fun ongoing exercise in Pattern Recognition and "meaningful coincidences." Have fun with it and every time you notice a Golden Ratio or Fibonacci Number, celebrate the wink you're receiving from the Universe.

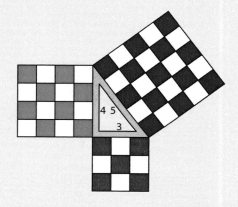

Pythagoras' Famous Fibonacci-Flavored 3-4-5 Triangle

Although Fibonacci delineated his famous Sequence (0,1,1,2,3,5,8,13,21…) in the 13th century, the imprint can be seen in Pythagoras' renowned 3-4-5 Triangle over a thousand years earlier. Study for a moment this classic graphical rendition of the Pythagorean Triangle. When you count the number of small colored squares within each of the 3 larger squares framing the Triangle, you'll notice something quite special about the revealed 3 numbers. Hint: Fibonacci would have approved. This exercise is described in Golden Ratio master Michael Schneider's *Fibonacci Numbers & Golden Mean Activity Book.*

Connect the D●ts for Greater Insight

Connecting the d●ts between or within diverse disciplines or data opens the door to greater understanding and insight. The example below uses key points of data taken from the book *The Golden Ratio Lifestyle Diet*, all revealing the hidden power of applying the Golden Ratio to one's health. Of course, the pattern revealed by the dots in this example is also the epitome of excellence: a 5-pointed Golden Ratio star. Go ahead—grab your pen and connect the d●ts...

How can you represent the 6 key facets of the Golden Ratio in one graphic?

This is the authors' integrated **Golden Ratio Icon**™ featuring six of the Golden Ratio's key facets: Golden Ratio, Rectangle, Spiral, Star, Triangle and Fibonacci Sequence.

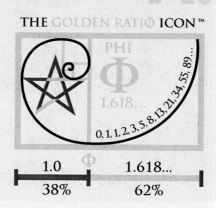

THE GOLDEN RATIO ICON ™

PHI
Φ
1.618...

0, 1, 1, 2, 3, 5, 8, 13, 21, 34, 55, 89, ...

1.0 Φ 1.618...
38% 62%

The Golden Ratio Workout Wave method uses alternating periods and intensities of workouts and recovery tuned to Fibonacci numbers. This supports healthy exercise and peak performance waves in any endeavor, while minimizing injury and burnout.

Buoyant posture, standing and sitting, supports the natural Golden Proportions of our spine and decompresses our organs.

Tuning one's nutrition to a Golden Ratio Zone of 40% carbs, 30% protein, 30% fat (all of optimal, organic quality) lowers inflammation, raises energy and improves health and longevity.

Ample lung capacity is the #1 predictor of healthy longevity. Golden Ratio breathing techniques, e.g., in a 3 to 5 inhale-to-exhale ratio, enhances oxygen utilization and extends life.

In a 24 hour day, a Golden Ratio of around 9 hours sleep or rest to 15 hours activity supports healthy digestion, hormonal balance and optimal health and longevity.

What does "Fib" refer to?

A great new poetry form with a Haiku twist invented by writer Greg Pincus. Fibs are usually 6-line, 20-syllable poems with a syllable count by line which follows the 1,1,2,3,5,8 Fibonacci Sequence, e.g., Pincus' first Fib:

One
Small,
Pre•cise,
Po•et•ic,
Spi•ral•ing mix•ture:
Math plus po•et•ry yields the Fib.

Now, your turn to tap into your inner Fibonacci poet; (numbers) = syllables per line:

(1) _____

(1) _____

(2) _____

(3) _____

(5) _____

(8) _____

What day is Phi Day?

There are actually *two* Phi Days in every year: June 18 (6.18) and August 13 (the 62% point in a year, which also happens to be consecutive numbers in the Fibonacci Sequence: 8/13).

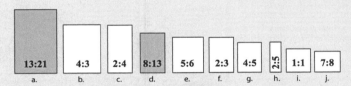

a.	b.	c.	d.	e.	f.	g.	h.	i.	j.
13:21	4:3	2:4	8:13	5:6	2:3	4:5	2:5	1:1	7:8

Dr. Fechner's Golden Rectangle Experiment
Answers to Dr. Fechner's Golden Rectangle Experiment.

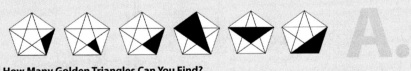

How Many Golden Triangles Can You Find?

Phyllotaxis describes plant's optimal, Fibonacci Sequence-resonant growth pattern. What does Phylotaxis (one "L") describe?

Artist and tech wizard Jonathan Harris' interactive news portal for *Seed* magazine, which integrates culture and science: www.Phylotaxis.com

How is the hat of most every wizard, witch, sorcerer and party reveler related to the Golden Ratio?

Wizard, witch, sorcerer and party reveler's hats are in the shape of a Golden Triangle.

What are the Golden Ratio secrets hidden-in-plain-sight with Audrey Tautou and her character Sophie in *The Da Vinci Code* film?

Audrey **Tau**tou and her character So**phi**e embody the two names ascribed to the Golden Ratio: **Tau** τ and **Phi** Φ.

Girl With a Watering Can

Vertical, horizontal and diagonal Golden Ratios all align perfectly on the watering can.

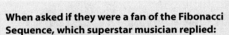

When asked if they were a fan of the Fibonacci Sequence, which superstar musician replied:

How can you not be? It's everywhere; it's all around…

Bono, U2's lead singer.

How is Kiefer Sutherland's character Martin Bohm in the Fox television series *Touch* related to the Golden Ratio?

The term *Golden Section* (in German, *Der Goldene Schnitt*) was first used in the 1835 2nd edition of the book *Die Reine Elementar-Mathematik*. The author's name? **Martin Ohm.**

What lightning-fast Olympian perfectly exemplifies the Golden Sleep Ratio by getting at least 9 hours of sleep every night?

Usain Bolt, 3-time World and Olympic gold medalist, "loads his catapult" by getting at least 9 hours sleep every night.

Further Learning Resources

You are the Universe, expressing itself as a human for a little while.

Eckhart Tolle

VIDEOS

The Golden Ratio Renaissance, TEDxEast talk (4 minutes) by Matthew Cross
  http://www.youtube.com/watch?v=0tAZe6pP-FM
Nature By Numbers, by Cristóbal Vila http://www.youtube.com/watch?v=kkGeOWYOFoA
Doodling in Math: Spirals, Fibonacci, and Being a Plant (3-part series), by Vi Hart
  http://www.youtube.com/user/Vihart
The Golden Ratio, by Sal Khan, Khan Academy: http://www.youtube.com/watch?v=5zosU6XTgSY
Disney's *Donald in Mathmagic Land*, DVD (27 minutes). Available for purchase online.

Videos viewable on YouTube by typing in the video's name (**bold**) into the YouTube Search Box.

WEB SITES

http://www.GoldenRatioLifestyle.com
http://www.GoldenRatioBook.com
http://www.TheDivineCode.com
http://www.MillionairesMap.com
http://www.PhiMatrix.com
http://www.ConstructingTheUniverse.com

Golden Ratio FaceBook Community: http://tinyurl.com/bjt3mzd

Dr. Robert Friedman's Online Golden Ratio Updates:
  http://paper.li/BobFriedmanMD/1340237453# or http://tinyurl.com/bhd57l9

BOOKS

The Golden Ratio Lifestyle Diet, by Robert Friedman, M.D. & Matthew Cross
The Divine Code of Da Vinci, Fibonacci, Einstein & YOU, by Matthew Cross & Robert Friedman, M.D.
The Genius Activation Quote Book, by Matthew Cross & Robert Friedman, M.D.
The Millionaire's Map, by Matthew Cross
Fibonacci Numbers And The Golden Mean, by Michael S. Schneider (wonderful must-read workbook)
The Golden Section: Nature's Greatest Secret, by Scott Olsen
The Wave Principle of Human Social Behavior and the New Science of Socionomics, by Robert R. Prechter, Jr.
The Golden Ratio: The Story of PHI, the World's Most Astonishing Number, by Mario Livio
Harmony: A New Way of Looking At Our World, by HRH Charles, The Prince of Wales
The Way Of The Labyrinth, by Helen Curry
The Power of Limits: Proportional Harmonies in Nature, Art, and Architecture, by Gyorgy Doczi
Blockhead: The Life of Fibonacci, by Joseph D'Agnese (wonderful storybook for children of all ages)
Growing Patterns, by Sarah Campbell (children's picture book, featured in the Fox TV series *Touch*)
The Eight, by Katherine Nelville (bestselling novel in which the Fibonacci Sequence plays a key role)
Fascinating Fibonaccis: Mystery & Magic in Numbers, by Trudi Hammel Garland
Fingerprints of the Gods, by Graham Hancock
The Da Vinci Code, by Dan Brown (particularly chapter 20, on PHI/The Golden Ratio)
Five Equations that Changed the World, by Dr. Michael Guillen (details Einstein's Fibonacci Sequence fascination)

Top of page: Fibonacci spiral leaf on a Rex Begonia 'Escargot' plant.

Practical Applications of the Golden Ratio & Fibonacci Sequence

When nature needs a proportion to relate things and to provide order on any scale, it tends to use the Golden Ratio.

Chris Pearson

Health, Diet, Nutrition, Exercise, Detoxification, Longevity, Beauty, Personal Development
http://www.GoldenRatioLifestyle.com
Rob Moses' PhysioStix Golden Ratio Training Tools: http://goldenspiralwellness.com/
Robert Walker's Golden Ratio Speed Theorem ~ *The Usain Bolt Guide To Blazing Speed*: http://www.nogym.net

Design
Golden Ratio Calipers, great hands-on tool. 3 excellent options:
New Zealand craftsman Nick Taylor: http://www.goldenmeancalipers.com
South American craftsman Javier Holodovsky: http://holyholo.com/caliper.htm
English dentist Dr. Eddy Levin: http://www.goldennumber.net/golden-mean-gauge/
Roger Dooley's Golden Ratio web design wisdom: http://www.RogerDooley.com

Abundance, Prosperity and Personal Growth http://www.MillionairesMap.com

Photography & General Software Design Tools/Apps
PhiMatrix™, for Golden Ratio web, photo and general design: http://www.PhiMatrix.com
Portrait Tips and Techniques, by Wayne Radford: http://www.portraittipsandtechniques.com
Camera Awesome, free iPhone® App for taking Golden Ratio pictures: http://www.CameraAwsome.com

Typography Golden Ratio Typography by Chris Pearson: http://www.pearsonified.com

Natural Beauty
Golden Ratio Eyebrow Sculpting System, by Anastasia Beverly Hills: http://www.Anastasia.net
Golden Ratio Dentistry, by Dr. David Frey: http://www.PerfectWhiteSmile.com

Music
Music from many classical composers contains Golden Ratios, e.g., Bach, Mozart, Debussey, Beethoven, Vivaldi, Telleman, Tchaikovsky; it is also frequently found in much modern popular music such as The Beatles.
David Ison's Golden Ratio-resonant therapeutic music for mind, body and soul: http://www.theisonmethod.com

Poetry/Haiku
Fibonacci poetry/haiku: Search "Fib (poetry)" on Wikipedia.org; Book: *The 14 Fibs of Gregory K.*, by Greg Pincus.

Stock Forecasting
Elliott Wave International, Robert R. Prechter, Jr.: http://www.ElliottWave.com
Elliott Wave Trader, Avi Gilburt: http://www.ElliottWaveTrader.net
Fibonacci Queen, Carolyn Boroden: http://www.FibonacciQueen.com

Time Golden Ratio Zen Alarm Clock: http://www.Now-Zen.com

Posters Fibonacci & Golden Ratio Posters: http://www.mathk-phd.com/posters.htm#

Woodworking
Fibonacci Gauge in Proportional Design, *Wood* Magazine with Jeff Mertz:
http://www.youtube.com/watch?v=5Xgw84Kwrh8

Fashion & Dress http://www.TheFashionCode.com

Acknowledgements

To our parents, Jan and Matt (Matthew) and Maxine and Jerald (Robert); our Golden Ratio Goddesses, Diana and Ari and to our families. We love you. 🔵

To the two Leonardo's: Fibonacci and Da Vinci; Fra Luca Pacioli, Pythagoras, Thomas Jefferson, Albert Einstein, John Michell, Michael S. Schneider, Scott Olsen, Scott Onstott, Stephen McIntosh, Gary Meisner, HRH Charles The Prince of Wales, Michael Castine, Peter Tompkins, Livio Stecchini, Dan Brown, John Martineau, Robert R. Prechter, Jr., Mario Livio, Nigel Reading, Dr. Gary Greenberg, Jain, Dr. W. Edwards Deming, R. Buckminster Fuller, Marshall Thurber, Clare Crawford and Robert Mason, Gyorgy Doczi, Dr. Eddy Levin, Tom Reczek, Frank Lloyd Wright, Ralph Nelson Elliott, The Beatles, Anastasia Soare, Monica Dean, Ruth & Sara Levy, Chloe Hedden, Jamie Wyeth, Dr. Barry Sears, Dr. Ronald Sandler, Dr. Michael Guillen, David Ison, Roger Hodgson, J.K. Rowling, Ron Howard, Tom Hanks, Audrey Tautou, Rob Morrow, David Krumholtz, Alex, Ioana and Andreea Samoilescu, Danielle Donello-Papandrea, Trudi Hammel Garland, Graham Hancock, Dawn Saidur, Dr. David Wright, Dave Scott, Casey Viator, Tim Kring, Keifer Sutherland, Dr. Mehmet Oz, Dr. Michael Roizen, Bjorn Borg, Tiger Woods, Steve Jobs, Steve Wozniak, Jonathan Ive, Walt Disney, John Lennon & Yoko Ono, John F. Kennedy, Michael Jackson, George Clooney, Sean Connery, Jennifer Lopez, Jennifer Lawrence, Marilyn Monroe, and all of the visionaries throughout history who were/are intrigued by and reflect the Golden Ratio/Fibonacci Sequence in their lives, work and legacy. To you, dear reader. Thank you for joining us on this Golden magical mystery tour. To infinity and beyond!

Illustration Credits

#: 5 Elements Diagram, http://en.wikipedia.org/wiki/File:Wuxing_en.svg **A:** AmExCard, graphic customization by Nikylla Celine. • Anastasia Soare, by Dana & Stephane Maitec; courtesy of Anastasia Soare: www.Anastasia.net • Apple logo with multiple Golden Ratio overlays: overlays are the Author's design, rendered by Tom Reczek; inspired by Saikat Banerjee/Banskt Designs • Apple iCloud® logo with Golden Ratio overlays, by Takamasa Matsumoto at Design Archive: http://stam-design-stam.blogspot.com/2011/06/law-of-beauty-hidden-behind-icloud-icon.html • Apple iOS 7 Icons Design Grid, with Golden Ratio overlay: overlay is the Author's design, rendered by Tom Reczek • Apple iPhone® and iOS 7 Photos Icon: www.Apple.com • Audrey Tautou, by Georges Biard: http://commons.wikimedia.org/wiki/File:Audrey_Tautou_Cannes_2012.jpg **B:** Beatles, by United Press International, photographer unknown/copyright free: http://commons.wikimedia.org/wiki/File:The_Beatles_in_America.JPG • Bjorn Borg, photographer unknown; provided rights-free to co-author Matthew Cross by Donnay USA PR representative at Hanover, NH 1985. • Bono, by and courtesy of Michael Castine • Buckminster Fuller, by Dan Lindsay: http://en.wikipedia.org/wiki/File:BuckminsterFuller1.jpg • Buckminsterfullerene, by Sponk/modified: http://commons.wikimedia.org/wiki/File:Buckminsterfullerene_animated.gif • Buddha, by Dirk Beyer: http://commons.wikimedia.org/wiki/File:Kamakura_Budda_Daibutsu_front_1885.jpg **C:** Casey Viator, courtesy of Casey Viator: www.CaseyViator.com • Chartres Cathedral, by Atlant: http://commons.wikimedia.org/wiki/File:Chartres_1.jpg • Chartres Labyrinth: http://www.starwheels.com/infopage.php?pagename=sacredlabyrinths **D:** Dave Scott, courtesy of Dave Scott: DaveScottInc.com • David by Michelangelo, by Rico Heil: http://commons.wikimedia.org/wiki/File:David_von_Michelangelo.jpg • Deming Prize, courtesy of the Japanese Union of Scientists & Engineers (JUSE), Tokyo, Japan. • Diagram of the Supreme Ultimate, by Thanato: http://commons.wikimedia.org/wiki/File:Yin_yang_laozi.jpg • Diatom by Steve Gschmeissner, from Getty Images • *Donald in Mathmagic Land*, Copyright © and Trademark The Walt Disney Co., www.Disney.com **E:** Eiffel Tower, by: Tryfon Kar: http://commons.wikimedia.org/wiki/User:Tryfkar **F:** Fashion Code, courtesy of Sara & Ruth Levy: www.TheFashionCode.com • Forbidden City, by Pvt pauline: http://commons.wikimedia.org/wiki/File:Maquette_van_de_Verboden_Stad_en_Jingshan_Park.JPG **G:** George Clooney, by Nicolas Genin: http://en.wikipedia.org/wiki/File:George_Clooney_66ème_Festival_de_Venise_(Mostra)_3Alt1.jpg • Golden Gate Bridge, by Rich Niewiroski Jr: http://en.wikipedia.org/wiki/File:GoldenGateBridge-001.jpg • Golden Angel/Rectangle/Spiral/ photography, by Wayne Radford: http://www.radfordphoto.com.au/ • Golden Ratio Icon™, with Robert Friedman, M.D.; rendered by Tom Reczek: www.618Design.com • Golden Ratio typography, by Chris Pearson: http://www.pearsonified.com/2011/12/golden-ratio-typography.php • Golden Snitch, by Rtphokie: http://commons.wikimedia.org/wiki/File:Golden_snitch.jpg • Great Pyramid, by Nina Bruker: http://en.wikipedia.org/wiki/File:Kheops-Pyramid.jpg **H:** Hair spiral: Special thanks to Connor Friedman • Heart Muscle, courtesy of J. Bell Pettigrew, The Bakken; Minneapolis, MN. • Hildegard von Bingen, by master stained glass artist Plamen Petrov: http://plamensart.com • Human Ear, Eye and Lexus, all with PhiMatrix Golden Ratio Grid overlay, courtesy of: www.PhiMatrix.com **I:** Imagine, John Lennon Memorial at Strawberry Fields in New York City's Central Park, by Matthew Cross **I:** Icosahedron, by Tomruen: http://en.wikipedia.org/wiki/File:Zeroth_stellation_of_icosahedron.png **J:** Jennifer Lawrence, by Mingle MediaTV: http://commons.wikimedia.org/wiki/File:Jennifer_Lawrence_at_the_83rd_Academy_Awards.jpg • Jennifer Lopez, by Tom Sorensen: http://en.wikipedia.org/wiki/File:Jennifer_Lopez_at_the_What_to_Expect_When_You%27re_Expecting_Premiere_2012_(Cropped)_2.png • Portrait of JFK (1967), painting in oil by and courtesy of Jamie Wyeth **K:** Kiefer Sutherland, by Kristin Dos Santos: http://commons.wikimedia.org/wiki/File:Kiefer_Sutherland_at_24_Redemption_premiere_4.jpg **L:** Leonardo Fibonacci, by Hans-Peter Postel: http://en.wikipedia.org/wiki/File:Leonardo_da_Pisa.jpg **M:** Marilyn Monroe, photographer unknown; studio publicity still from *Niagara*, 20th Century Fox/copyright free: http://commons.wikimedia.org/wiki/File:Marilyn_Monroe_in_Niagara.jpg • Mario Merz neon Golden Spiral art installation at the Forum in Rome by Claudio Abate: www.ClaudioAbate.com • Matthew Cross: Winning race, by: Peter Wnek, www.PeterWnekPhoto.com; Author's photo, by: Diana Doroftei; Strength training, by: Cerasela Feraru. • Dr. Mehmet Oz, by David Shankbone: http://commons.wikimedia.org/wiki/File:Dr_Oz_(cropped).png • Michael Jackson, by the White House Photo Office: http://commons.wikimedia.org/wiki/File:Michael_Jackson_with_the_Reagans.jpg • Monica Dean, by Giuliano Bekor; courtesy of Monica Dean **N:** Gold nano-particle, by Materialscientist: http://en.wikipedia.org/wiki/File:Twin2.jpg • Nautilus shell, by Chris 73: http://commons.wikimedia.org/wiki/File:NautilusCutawayLogarithmicSpiral.jpg • Notre Dame Cathedral, by Sanchezn: http://en.wikipedia.org/wiki/File:NotreDameDeParis.jpg **P:** Parthenon, by Harrieta171: http://commons.wikimedia.org/wiki/File:2006_01_21_Athènes_Parthénon.JPG • Platonic Solids, by JovanCormac: http://commons.wikimedia.org/wiki/File:Platonic_Solids_Stereo_4_-_Dodecahedron.gif • Portrait of JFK, by and courtesy of the artist Jamie Wyeth • Pyramid of the Sun, by Wernervp: http://en.wikipedia.org/wiki/File:Pyramid_of_the_sun_teotihuacan_with_crowd.jpg • Pythagoras 3-4-5 Triangle, courtesy of Scott Onstott: www.ScottOnstott.com **Q:** Quasicrystal, by J.W. Evans: http://en.wikipedia.org/wiki/File:Quasicrystal1.jpg **R:** Ratio sculpture, by: IsraCast: http://schools-wikipedia.org/images/229/22964.jpg.htm • Rob Moses with Physiostix: Courtesy Rob Moses **S:** Sand Grains, courtesy of Gary Greenberg: www.sandgrains.com • Spiral hands: http://www.tumc.org • Rex Begonia 'Escargot' plant page 56 by: Cerasela Feraru • Steve Jobs, by Matthew Yohe: http://commons.wikimedia.org/wiki/File:Steve_Jobs_Headshot_2010 CROP.jpg • Steve Wozniak, by Andy Hertzfeld: http://en.wikipedia.org/wiki/File:Joey_Slotnick_%26_Steve_Wozniak.jpg • Sean Connery: Still from the public domain/copyright-free film trailer from the 1964 Alfred Hitchcock film *Marnie* **T:** Taj Mahal, by: Shivam592: http://commons.wikimedia.org/wiki/File:Taj_Mahal_in_Sunny_Day.jpg • Tiger Woods, by James Phelps: http://en.wikipedia.org/wiki/File:TigerWoods2004RyderCup3.jpg • Superman emblem: http://en.wikipedia.org/wiki/File:Superman_shield.png **U:** Usain Bolt, by Erik van Leeuwen: http://commons.wikimedia.org/wiki/File:Usain_Bolt_smiling_Berlin_2009.JPG **V:** Venus de Milo, by Michal Osmenda: http://commons.wikimedia.org/wiki/File:Aphrodite_of_Milos_at_the_Louvre_Museum_in_Paris.jpg • Venus Orbit, courtesy of John Martineau: www.WoodenBooks.com • Vitruvian Woman, by Chloe Hedden, Copyright © and commissioned by the authors **W:** Widescreen 16x10 display, by florisla: http://en.wikipedia.org/wiki/File:LG_L194WT-SF_LCD_monitor.jpg • Wright Balance, courtesy of Dr. David Wright: www.WrightBalance.com **Z:** Zeckendorf Theorem, by Incnis Mrsi: http://en.wikipedia.org/wiki/File:Zeckendorf_representations.png • Zen Alarm Clock, courtesy of Stephen McIntosh: www.Now-Zen.com

About the Authors

Matthew Cross

is President of Leadership Alliance, an international consulting firm providing breakthrough strategies for growth and transformation. A founding partner of the Leading Edge Performance Institute, Matthew is a Deming Quality Scholar, Hoshin Kanri strategic alignment specialist, thought leader and speaker working with Fortune 100 companies around the world.

Matthew began researching the practical applications of the Golden Ratio at age 13. In addition to co-authoring *The Golden Ratio Lifestyle Diet, The Divine Code of Da Vinci, Fibonacci, Einstein & YOU* and *The Divine Code Genius Activation Quote Book* with Robert Friedman, M.D., Matthew is the author of *The Millionaire's MAP, The Hoshin Success Compass* and *Be Your Own President.* He is also an ancient history explorer and competitive athlete (running and tennis), with a deep belief in everyone's unique genius and unlimited potential. Matthew can be reached at: MCross@GoldenRatioLifestyle.com. Follow him on Twitter: @MatthewKCross • *www.about.me/matthewcross*

Robert Friedman, M.D.

practiced nutritional and preventive medicine in Santa Fe, New Mexico for twenty five years before turning his attention to the application of the Golden Ratio to health and longevity.

He co-authored with Matthew Cross *The Divine Code of Da Vinci, Fibonacci, Einstein & YOU*, a 660 page tour-de-force on the Golden Ratio, which allows anyone to access the Code and apply it in their chosen field. That book's success inspired two other Golden Ratio-based books: *The Divine Code Genius Activation Quote Book* and *The Golden Ratio Lifestyle Diet.* Dr. Friedman is also the originator of Spiral~Chi and co-originator of Yogaia, both evolutionary movement systems based on spinal and spiral waves. They have been compared to a synthesis of yoga and tai-chi and emphasize tuning in to one's spiral-wave nature for regeneration and rejuvenation. Dr. Friedman can be reached at DrBob@GoldenRatioLifestyle.com. Follow him on Twitter: @BobFriedmanMD *www.about.me/robertfriedmanm.d.*

The authors are available for speaking presentations and interviews.
Contact: Speaker@HoshinMedia.com • 1.203.322.1456

Index

FROM HOSHIN MEDIA

Made in the USA
Middletown, DE
17 September 2015